PLUTO

Pipe-Line Under The Ocean

The Definitive Story by
Adrian Searle

Shanklin Chine 1995

Published by Shanklin Chine
12 Pomona Road, Shanklin
Isle of Wight PO37 6PF

Produced by Crossprint Design & Print
Newport, Isle of Wight PO30 5XB

CONTENTS

Dedicated to all those who took part in Operation PLUTO and who achieved so much in such a short time.

FOREWORD

**by the Rt. Hon. Lord Prior, PC
Chairman, The General Electric Company plc**

That Operation PLUTO was one of the outstanding engineering achievements of the Second World War is beyond question.

It was a wholly British achievement, devised and developed by British engineers, using equipment produced by British firms - with some valuable manufacturing assistance from our American allies.

Many of those firms later became part of the General Electric Company, and I am therefore pleased to be given the opportunity of adding a tribute from the present-day GEC management to the skill, ingenuity and dedication of all those who rose to the immense challenge posed by the startling concept of an undersea petroleum pipe-line on the bed of the English Channel, capable of delivering millions of gallons of fuel to the Allied armies in Normandy and - eventually - all the way to Germany itself.

Peacetime commercial rivalries between firms such as the cable producers Siemens Brothers - who were, in fact, a former German factory - and W.T. Henley's Telegraph Works Company - who are part of GEC, and whose contribution to PLUTO was equally vital - were totally submerged in the common cause of successfully developing the concept for PLUTO's masters, the Petroleum Warfare Department.

It was a marvellous example of how our nation pulled together to form a united front in the face of adversity and common challenge.

Possibly because a pipe-line is essentially a prosaic object, largely unseen and uninspiring to the eye - unlike, for example, the floating prefabricated Mulberry harbours - PLUTO has perhaps not received its due recognition in the context of our wartime victory.

There may be arguments over its eventual value to the great military offensive. but, in engineering terms - and in terms of enterprise, dedication and common endeavour - there can be no argument whatsoever that PLUTO was an extraordinary success.

The people who conceived, developed and delivered the Pipe-Line Under The Ocean to the Allied push for victory in 1944-45 are worthy of our tribute 50 years on. Mr. Searle's book fills an important gap in our appreciation of the events which eventually led to Victory in Europe.

Stanhope Gate, London,
April 1995

INTRODUCTION

The 50th anniversary of the Allied war victory in Europe is a fitting time to pay tribute to Operation PLUTO, the extraordinary Pipe-Line Under The Ocean project which helped to fuel the advance of the liberating armies from the Normandy invasion beaches. This book is intended to provide that tribute - for PLUTO was a remarkable achievement, described by General Eisenhower as "second only in daring to the (Mulberry) artificial harbours." The idea of a submarine pipe-line capable of delivering fuel supplies across the English Channel in time of war was regarded by many as a preposterous concept when it was first suggested in 1942. Fortunately, there were those who refused to allow their initial scepticism - for they must surely have been sceptical at the start - to override their enthusiasm, energy, enterprise and flair for the unorthodox. The impossible was achieved with PLUTO.

There is often confusion when references are made to Operation PLUTO. Specifically, it related to *both* the cross-Channel pipe-lines to Cherbourg and Boulogne from, respectively, the Isle of Wight and Kent - although it is sometimes only the former route which is credited with the PLUTO code-name, while the Boulogne route is described as DUMBO. The truth is that both were conceived as part of the same overall operation. DUMBO was indeed the specific name for the Boulogne pipe-line - but as part of PLUTO, in the same way as BAMBI was the code-name for the Cherbourg route. Together, the two Channel routes constitute the principal concern of this book. However, the pipe-line network which extended beyond the French terminals, eventually reaching Germany itself, was essentially an extension of the PLUTO operation, and therefore also has a place in the story.

This work provides the first comprehensive account in book form of this highly ingenious wartime operation. Whatever the arguments over the operational success, or otherwise, of PLUTO - examined within these pages - they should not obscure recognition of an incredible feat of engineering, and the people who brought about its execution.

Adrian Searle,
Bembridge, Isle of Wight
April 1995

Chapter 1
1941-42: MOUNTBATTEN'S REQUIREMENT

A reluctant appointee

Although it was not to wag its tail triumphantly until the dramatic closing stages of the Second World War, Operation PLUTO - the Disney-esque canine acronym for the extraordinary Pipe-Line Under the Ocean project - was conceived at a time when, in the minds of most Britons, invasion was still something to be feared rather than anticipated.

In searching for PLUTO origins, the first date of significance is 10 October 1941, the day Lord Louis Mountbatten, soon after taking command of the aircraft carrier HMS *Illustrious*, received a message at sea from Prime Minister Winston Churchill. "We want you home here at once for something which you will find of the highest interest," was the text of Churchill's signal. Reporting to London, Mountbatten was told the Prime Minister wished him to succeed Admiral of the Fleet Lord Keyes as the head of Britain's Combined Operations. Mountbatten, at 41, was a reluctant appointee - a young Naval captain whose instincts demanded a quick return to the fleet at sea.

Lord Louis Mountbatten, Chief of Combined Operations, whose extraordinary idea for a pipe-line under the 'ocean' was turned into extraordinary fact.

But Churchill dug in his heels, and Mountbatten - as he was later to admit - gave in. The Prime Minister's directive for his new Combined Ops chief stressed the need to continue with commando raids in order to gain vital experience of landing on enemy-held coasts, and to harass the occupying German forces. Such operations were also important in the context of boosting morale or, as Churchill put it to Mountbatten, "in order to keep up the offensive spirit" - at a time when defensive measures were still very much the routine of the day. Offence was also at the heart of the main task assigned to Lord Louis by Churchill on that autumn day in 1941.

The Prime Minister ordered Mountbatten to begin preparations straight away for a counter-invasion of occupied Europe. Forces in over-whelming numbers would need to be put ashore in France, sufficient in strength and resources to defeat the Germans and begin the advance which would ultimately liberate the continent from Nazi tyranny.

Mountbatten was charged with developing the whole philosophy of the great invasion. It would, Churchill told him, call for the closest co-oper-ation between the three armed services, both in the planning stages of the operation, and in the actual execution - and it would also require a con-siderable degree of innovation. "You must devise and design new landing craft, appurtenances and appliances, and train the three services to act together as a single force in combined operation," Lord Louis was instructed.

His initial reluctance now submerged by such inspirational talk from the Prime Minister, Mountbatten set about his new job with tremendous enthusiasm and dynamism. Churchill's faith in Lord Louis' ability to cut through inter-service rivalry and concentrate minds on the mighty task in hand was not misplaced. His appointment was to prove a stroke of genius - the first in a long line along the road to the conception and development of PLUTO.

The germ of an idea

In wrestling with the awesome problems of landing a huge assault force in France, Mountbatten had, by the spring of 1942, reached two major decisions which were to have a direct bearing on the eventual conception of the PLUTO project.

Firstly, he had quickly concluded that he could not rely on the capture of a Continental port equipped with complete oil storage and discharge facilities for ocean-going oil tankers. He had, therefore, ordered tests on an alternative means of supplying the Allied forces of liberation with the oil and petrol to fuel their advance across Europe. The scheme involved the pulling of short pipe-lines from the invasion beaches to a sufficient depth of water in which small coastal tankers could discharge, via the pipes, into tanks which would be built on or near the shore.

Preliminary trials were held at the North Devon resort of Westward Ho!, where sea conditions were similar to those along the French coast - but Mountbatten was already having second thoughts. The envisaged transfer of fuel from the tankers to the shore, he concluded, would be at the mercy of the weather - and the Luftwaffe. It was too risky. Indeed, the traditional use of oil tankers in any form would be inviting trouble in the anchorages and the approaches to them - from dive bombers, fighter planes and U-boats alike. Mountbatten went back to the drawing board.

Geoffrey Lloyd, Britain's Secretary for Petroleum, pictured in wartime. His enthusiasm and drive got the PLUTO project off the ground.
(IWM)

In April 1942, he was watching a demonstration of flame-throwing at Moody Down, Hampshire, with Geoffrey Lloyd, Britain's Secretary for Petroleum and, since 1940, the Minister in charge of the Petroleum Warfare Department. Lord Louis's thoughts were elsewhere. Still deeply concerned at the obvious vulnerability of the oil tankers - and therefore the entire operation - to heavy bombardment off the invasion beaches, he turned to Lloyd. "Could you run a pipe-line under the Channel to supply oil when we invade?" the Minister was asked. In that single, to-the-point, question, the seeds for the pup that would be PLUTO were sown.

Chapter 2
1942: HARTLEY'S SOLUTION

Lloyd takes up the challenge

On the face of it, Mountbatten's query seemed an extraordinary suggestion, and certainly not the response Lloyd had expected when he had enquired of Lord Louis whether there was anything more the Petroleum Division could do to assist the invasion plans. Yet, this was clear, and inspired, thinking on the part of the Chief of Combined Ops. He simply could not risk the destruction of vital oil and petrol supplies before they had even reached France, and the knock-on consequences of attacks on tankers berthed off the landing beaches bore the potential for numbing disaster.

A submarine pipe-line stretched right across the Channel was an incredible alternative, but it made a lot of sense. The problem was - could it be done?

Fortunately, Geoffrey Lloyd, three months past his 40th birthday, had a relish for novel ideas. In July 1940, in the wake of Dunkirk, his enthusiasm for the potential of petroleum-induced flame as a weapon of war had led to the establishment of the Petroleum Warfare Department. At that time, of course, Lloyd had not been entertaining thoughts of assisting a cross-Channel offensive. His energies in 1940 were entirely directed towards the development of a repellent against the very real threat of a German invasion from the newly-acquired springboard of Northern France.

In the event, the static flame weapons developed by the PWD for the defence of Southern England, and other vulnerable coastal areas, were not called upon to prove their worth - although techniques developed by the Department were later used to considerable effect as the tide of war turned in favour of Britain and her allies.

Given his enthusiasm for the unorthodox, Geoffrey Lloyd's reaction in 1942 to Mountbatten's radical idea for an undersea cross-Channel pipe-line was entirely in keeping. Lord Louis had conceded with a fine degree of understatement that it would be "a bit difficult," yet Lloyd, whatever his initial misgivings, took the suggestion on board and immediately set about the task of implementation. He raised the matter firstly with the experts in his Department, and then with those who were advising them on the construction of the oil pipe-line system, by then well under way, connecting the Bristol Channel, the Mersey and the Thames. Through this 1,000-mile network flowed bulk supplies of petrol from the West Coast tanker ports to fuel, respectively, the defensive and offensive operations of Britain's front line fighter and bomber airfields in the South of England.

That was one thing. Laying a pipe-line flexible enough to lie on the seabed and strong enough to resist leaks as currents hurled it against the rocks, was quite another. On land, service gangs constantly patrolled the area over which pipe-lines were laid to check for - and repair - leaks. There would, of course, be no chance of that with a pipe-line on the bed of the English Channel. Then there was the matter of pressure - two types of it. An undersea pipe-line would have to contend not only with the pressure at which the oil and petrol had to be pumped in order to move it mile by mile, but also with the external pressure of the seawater - and, at 600 feet, that pressure was equal to 300 lb per square inch. That was heavy pressure in anyone's language. The experts collectively shook their heads.

To this initial, and entirely understandable, scepticism, they added the warning that tidal conditions and the depth of water in the Channel would mean a long, complex and hazardous pipe-laying operation. Heavy moorings and large flotillas of craft would be required if any of the known methods of laying submarine oil-lines were to be used. Such conspicuous and pro-

Clifford Hartley, the 'father' of PLUTO, who produced an unorthodox, ingenious and ultimately successful answer to the poser set by Mountbatten in 1942.

longed activity would be hopelessly vulnerable to enemy attack. It was clear to Lloyd from an early stage: if Mountbatten's requirement for an undersea pipe-line was to be met, a novel solution - or solutions - to the problems of achieving it would have to be found.

Hartley and the hollow cable

Cometh the hour, cometh the man ... and in this case he came to Geoffrey Lloyd's Ministerial offices on 15 April 1942 in the guise of Clifford Hartley, the gifted 53-year-old Chief Engineer of the Anglo-Iranian Oil Company, for whom he had worked since 1924.

Hartley, who had not been among those consulted, had not even heard of the proposed pipe-line before his arrival that day for a meeting of the Overseas Development Committee of the Oil Control Board. By lucky chance - as it transpired - he had been asked to go to the meeting by his Chairman, Sir William Fraser, Honorary Petroleum Adviser to the War Office, who was unable to attend. After the meeting, in discussion with Dr. George Lees, the Committee's Secretary, and A. C. (later Sir Alfred) Hearn, its Chairman, Hartley could hardly fail to notice a large chart of the English Channel spread out over a long table in their office.

According to Norman Kemp, writing in 1956 on *The Devices of War*, Hartley's inquisitiveness got the better of him. "What's that for?" he

Dr. H. R. Wright, Managing-Director of Siemens Brothers, who put his company's full weight behind the PLUTO project. (Charles Brown)

asked. "Mountbatten wants a pipe-line across the Channel," he was told. "It's devilish urgent!"

If we accept Kemp's version of events, Hartley took the 'urgent' message to heart there and then, astonishing Lees and Hearn by suggesting a solution within a few minutes of being confronted with a problem which had been baffling others for days. He suggested to Geoffrey Lloyd that probably the only means of successfully implementing Mountbatten's idea would be to devise a method of constructing a pipe in one complete length - and one which could be laid at

16

An aerial view of Siemens' Woolwich Works on the Thames, where the first trial lengths of HAIS cable - and much of what followed - were made. Although this picture was taken in the immediate post-war period, the layout was virtually the same during the war years.
(Charles Brown)

sufficient speed to combat the strong Channel currents. Methods used for manufacturing and laying submarine telegraphy cable could be adapted to produce high-pressure oil lines. The principal adaptation would be the omission of the cable's central copper core and insulation, but there would be a need for strong armour if the lead sheaths were to withstand the high internal pressure. Hartley added that multiple lines could be laid to deliver the quantity of fuel required, "with the advantage," as he was later to put it, "of not having all the eggs in one basket."

It was certainly a remarkable idea, but Hartley was able to call on a measure of relevant practical experience. He recalled his company's successful pre-war use of small (three-inch) diameter pipes, worked at very high (1,500 lb/sq) pressure, to deliver more than 100,000 gallons a day - the equivalent to 25,000 jerricans - through 40 miles of hilly terrain in Iran.

Unanimous and immediate approval for Hartley's proposal to be tested

17

in trials was provided by the Committee. "The utmost encouragement was given to the development of the idea," wrote Hartley later, "and it was undertaken as a matter of the highest priority by the Anglo-Iranian Oil Company."

Promised every co-operation by Sir William Fraser, Hartley's first move was to approach Dr. H. R. Wright, Managing-Director of Siemens Brothers & Co. Ltd., at Woolwich, with a request for that company to design and produce a trial length of pipe-line in order to test the technical feasibility of the plan. "Dr. Wright received the idea with enthusiasm," Hartley recalled. Certainly, Siemens wasted no time in coming up with the goods.

"A design was prepared based on the knowledge gained in the development of gas pressure power cables, combined with our long experience of the requirements for submarine cable practice," wrote E. A. Beavis, of Siemens' Cable Test and Development Department, in 1946. "Within a few days, an experimental length of 200 yards had been made from materials available in stock, and was undergoing tests."

The first acronyms

Before a week had passed, the experimental pipe-line, just two inches in diameter, and designed to withstand a working pressure of about 500 lb/sq, had been sufficiently tested for Hartley to describe the results as "very promising." For reasons of security, the pipe was officially designated a 'cable' and given a code-name, with the initials of Hartley, Anglo-Iranian and Siemens combined to form the acronym HAIS.

A little later in 1942 - sources are vague on the point - the overall project was officially code-named Operation PLUTO, although secrecy demanded that only those involved at the highest level were made aware of this at the time. There is general acceptance that the acronym from the outset represented the initial letters of Pipe-Line Under The Ocean, and that Pluto, mythological ruler of the realms of the dead, was probably a minor factor in its choice - it is Disney's animated dog which is more popularly associated with the project[1]. However, two variations on the full

[1] *But see Chapter 8*

title tend to crop up both in official records and published works. The first is minor - the substitution of the plural 'Lines' for the singular 'Line' - but the second variation is substantially different, lesss poetic, yet markedly more specific: Pipe-Line Underwater Transport of Oil. This is used either as the substantive version (for example, in the official *History of the Second World War - Civil Histories Series*, published by HMSO) or as an alternative to Pipe-Line Under The Ocean (as in Naval Historical Branch records at the Ministry of Defence).

The truth is almost certainly that, once the PLUTO acronym had been accepted - irrespective of what was specifically on the mind of whoever came up with it in the first place - it mattered little what the initials actually stood for. As it progressed, Operation PLUTO was officially referred to as exactly that. It was good enough.

Pluto ... the cartoon inspiration for the pipe-line's code-name. (Walt Disney Inc)

Chapter 3
1942-43: CABLE ON TRIAL

The early tests

The first experimental section of HAIS cable, reinforced with two layers of steel tape and armoured with heavy galvanised steel wire, would have delivered only some 30,000 gallons a day across the 20 nautical miles then visualised for operational purposes - and a great deal more than that was required. The tests continued. Before a further week had passed, the cable had been handled to and from a Post Office cable ship, and tested satisfactorily for strength. Samples were now shown by a

Extruded lengths of lead pipe coiled down to the rear of the armouring machine at Woolwich Works. The coil in the foreground is being fed into the armourer, while the middle coil is taken across the workshop from the 2,000-ton lead extrusion press. Each coil was jointed simultaneously to form a continuous 30-mile length. (Charles Brown)

*Another view of the lead piping being fed down the coil at Woolwich Works.
(Charles Brown)*

delighted Geoffrey Lloyd to Service chiefs and to the Prime Minister. "Instructions were received," recalled Clifford Hartley, "to proceed with its development with all speed."

Involvement in the pipe-line project was now broadened to include the Post Office, the Admiralty, Combined Operations and the War Office, whose representatives met with Anglo-Iranian's to discuss the manufacture of further lengths, and to draw up a comprehensive test programme. Anglo-Iranian undertook, as agents of the Ministry of Fuel and Power's Petroleum Division, to develop, order, progress and supervise the construction of the pipe-line and all its attendant parts, plus the pumping installations and other structures. Siemens Brothers, with unbounded enthusiasm, immediately set about providing further cable - without even waiting for official orders!

On 10 May an 1,100-yard length of HAIS cable was loaded into the Post Office Telegraph Ship *Alert* and laid in the River Medway at Chatham. The lay was in the form of a loop so that high-pressure pumping tests could be carried out. Hartley had used all his persuasive powers to borrow the pumps for the test from the Manchester Ship Canal Company (who had installed them in the canal for the emergency operation of lock-gates in the event of air-raid damage). All went well to begin with, pumping tests at a pressure of 600 lb/sq producing the calculated

21

A full view of the heavy-duty Siemens armouring machine producing continuous 30-mile lengths of HAIS cable. (Charles Brown)

delivery of oil. Then, after three days and nights, falling deliveries indicated leaks. When compressed air was fed into the cable, three faulty sections were located.

The offending parts were cut out for examination by both the Post Office and Siemens, and also by W.T. Henley's Telegraph Works Company, who had been brought into the project - at Siemens' suggestion - in order to add further manufacturing capacity. The leaks were traced to sections of the cable where the upper steel reinforcing tape had slipped back during manufacture to leave gaps. Through these, as a result of the pumping pressure over the three days and nights of the test, the internal lead tubing had been exposed. This was the first major hitch in the pipe-line project, but it was to provide an early example of the spirit of co-operation between organisations - rivals in peacetime - which characterised PLUTO throughout.

Siemens and Henley's immediately combined their research and design facilities, working with the Post Office and the National Physical Laboratory - who had been brought in as advisors - to prepare new specifications within just two days of the failure. The two original layers of reinforcing tape were increased to four. Fears that this might seriously reduce flexibility and lead to problems when running the cable over the sheaves of a cable-laying ship proved unfounded. The flexibility remained, and the HAIS cable, with its enhanced reinforcement, could now be tested at higher working pressures. Orders were placed with

22

Siemens and Henley's for further lengths, and attention then turned to Scotland.

The Clyde trials

In June, test lengths of cable from both firms were laid by the Post Office Telegraph Ship *Iris* in deep water off the River Clyde. Tested first, the Siemens length was subjected to the severest possible conditions. Laid over the bow while the ship was moving forwards, its ends were capped, and the lead pipe was filled with air at normal atmospheric pressure. On the sea bed, some 200 feet below, it had to contend with outside pressures around six times greater. After recovery, it was pumped full of water for pressure-testing - and seemed in places to be leaking .

The cable was examined back at Woolwich, and the lead pipe within it, although unbroken, was found to have collapsed into the shape of a kidney as a result of the external pressure during the deep water test. Siemens discovered that water, forced through the steel wires and tapes, had become trapped between the deformed lead pipe and the cable

Number I coiling shed at Woolwich, showing the cable dropping down for coiling by a six-man crew. It was coiled for reasons of safety, protection, and ease of feeding into the cable ships' hauling gear and holds. (Charles Brown)

23

armouring. The pressure-testing after recovery had returned the pipe to its circular form and pushed the trapped water through the outer armouring. Thus, the impression of leaks had been wrongly created.

While the reason for the apparent failure of the Siemens' cable was being investigated, the length manufactured by Henley's was tested under much easier conditions. Like the Siemens length, it was laid from the bow of the *Iris* , but with the ship going astern to simulate the easier 'over-

A coil line of HAIS cable rises in height during storage at Woolwich. An idea of how high the coils were can be gauged by the comparative height of the worker within it. (Charles Brown)

the-stern' laying operation. The cable was laid full of water under 100 lb/sq internal pressure to balance the external pressure of the water. The lay was a total success. When examination of the Siemens cable showed that, far from being a failure, the first lay had actually withstood the most stringent of tests, it, too, was declared a success.

24

A finished coil - almost 12 feet high. (Charles Brown)

The decision was now taken to begin the manufacture of six operational lengths of HAIS cable, each of them 30 miles long, and to use one of the lengths for a full-scale trial in the Bristol Channel - where tidal conditions and the depth of water more severe than those in the English Channel could be found. It was the next best thing to a trial in the sea between England and France itself - which would obviously have invited potentially disastrous enemy intervention from sea and air.

Before this major trial could proceed, several lessons learnt from the earlier experiments had to be put into practice. Firstly, it was decided that, in order to avoid future risk of damage through the collapse of the lead piping, all cables should be filled with water and maintained - during manufacture and for all subsequent operations - at a constant internal pressure of between 100 and 200 lb/sq.

Secondly, a decision was needed on the manufacture of the lead piping itself, as the cable-makers - Siemens, Henley's and the other manufacturers by now enlisted in the cause - employed several different methods. Siemens conceded that their standard technique, involving a longitudinal seam - perfectly satisfactory for ordinary cable - would need some development to make it suitable for the pipe-line. Commendably, the company did not seek the time to make that development. Instead, recognising the need to avoid unnecessary delay, they agreed to the universal use of seamless lead tubing - and that meant somebody else's.

25

Commander Treby Heale, RNR, who skippered the Holdfast in the 1942 laying trials in the Bristol Channel. A man with virtually unrivalled experience of heavy submarine cable-laying, he later commanded HMS Latimer on her historic operational runs across the Channel. (IWM)

But whose? The cable works of Pirelli General was a contender, but tests on the lead piping made by its continuous presses were cut dramatically short when the works was damaged by enemy action. Pirelli's lead presses - in both Britain and the USA - would eventually contribute successfully to Operation PLUTO (as, indeed, would Siemens' standard vertical hydraulic presses), when the demand for cable increased, but it was Henley's who were chosen in 1942 to meet the initial manufacturing need for the lead pipe. The company's 'straight-through' method of manufacture on the 'Judge' horizontal lead press - named after the senior company operative under whose direction it had evolved - was the sole provider of the piping until operational requirements demanded greater manufacturing capacity and, thus, the involvement of other cable companies in the process.

Connecting the cable

A third major issue for resolution was the method to be adopted for the operational laying of the cable at sea. From an early stage it had been recognised that special cable ships would be needed, equipped to carry a sufficient coiled length of the unusually heavy cable - and there was the added problem of dealing with the shore ends in shallow water, into which the cable ships could not operate.

It was time for a 21-year-old old British coaster to make a - new - name for herself. Requisitioned from the Dundee, Perth & London Line, the 1,500-ton SS *London* was made available to the pipe-line project by the Admiralty and the Ministry of War Transport. The old ship was practically gutted, then re-built and fitted-out for her novel new role under the direction of the Director of Naval Construction. Equipped with Johnson & Phillips' cable gear, lent by the Post Office, in order to carry the 30-mile length of two-inch cable, she was renamed HMS *Holdfast*.

The problem of attaching the shore ends to the main cable was again resolved by close co-operation - this time between several commercial firms and the Admiralty Research Laboratory, working together at Siemens' Woolwich base. The requirement was for a cable joint which could be fastened in a short time, and which could cope with both rough handling and high pressure. The result of the team's labours was the ingenious HAIS cable coupling, devised jointly by Siemens Works Manager G. W. Giffin, H. W. Tombs - whose knowledge of the HAIS cable system was probably unrivalled - and Hartley himself. While it took between three and four hours (or just two, according to Siemens, if the job was entrusted to a skilled mechanic) to fit the bolt-less device to a cable end, trials demonstrated that two ends already fitted could be joined together at sea in only 20 minutes.

Bursting-discs of thin copper sheet, designed to burst and peal open under operating conditions, were incorporated in the joint to hold the internal waterpressure - of up to 200 lb/sq - at which the cable was now maintained during handling, storing and laying. The diameter of the coupling was sufficiently reduced and faired into the cable to allow it to be handled by the cable ship's machinery. In its final form, the HAIS coupling was both leakproof and incapable of inaccurate assembly. Once its development was complete, Siemens set up a training centre in Woolwich Works, at which the Army and Navy personnel earmarked for operational requirements were trained in assembling and fitting the device. Skilled mechanics were also sent by the company to other areas of the country to train Navy personnel on the spot[1].

The Bristol Channel experiment

Static tests on the cable itself continued at the manufacturers' premises, and pressures in excess of 3,000 lb/sq were maintained for several months. Throughout the autumn of 1942, Combined Operations con-

[1] *See Appendices*

ducted tests from an experimental establishment at Westward Ho! in an effort to find ways of handling the shore-end sections of the cable, using the type of craft which were likely to be available at the landing beaches after D-Day. "The most promising method devised was to mount two cable drums with about 1,000 yards of cable on horizontal axles in LCTs (tank landing craft), with a view to paying the cable out over the bow ramp, which was lowered with the craft going astern," recalled Hartley.

This was the method used when the full-scale rehearsal finally took place on 29 December 1942, out of Swansea, with the *Holdfast*. In charge of the newly-converted ship - at his company's suggestion - was the well-known and enormously respected Commander Treby Heale, RNR, who had been master of Siemens' famous cable-layer *Faraday*, sunk by enemy action earlier in the war, and had virtually unrivalled experience in the laying of heavy submarine cable. *Holdfast* successfully laid the 30-mile HAIS cable in the Bristol Channel at a speed of five knots, but great difficulty was experienced in laying the shore ends - at Swansea and Ilfracombe - owing to the LCT's lack of manoeuvrability when going astern with heavy cable over the bow. Priority was given to solving this problem.

In January 1943 a conference of Service chiefs at Combined Operations HQ agreed the best answer was to adopt the successful commercial practice of coiling sufficient cable horizontally in the hold of a self-propelled barge, specially fitted for paying it out over the stern through hand-controlled compressor gear. A Thames barge - the only type of craft reckoned to be suitable for the task - was released with her crew from vital work on the river, and adapted to carry the gear - and the troublesome shore ends were completed in just a few days' work at the end of March.

Meanwhile, back at Swansea, National Oil Refineries, the Royal Engineers and the Royal Army Service Corps' specially-trained bulk petroleum companies, had built a pumping station on the sea wall at Queens Dock, and connected it to their petrol tanks. With the assistance of the Petroleum Board, and help from both Combined Operations and the RASC, the RE had also erected a receiving terminal, complete with tanks, pumps and loading racks, at Watermouth Bay, near Ilfracombe.

With everything now in place, tests were carried out on the cable, using water in the pipe. When this was successfully pumped across the channel to the new terminal, the scene was set for the first petrol to flow through a full-length HAIS cable. On 4 April 1943, the pumps were set in motion at Swansea - and the petrol was successfully dispatched along the 30-mile pipe-line to Watermouth. Geoffrey Lloyd travelled down from London a few days later to witness a repeat performance. "He saw the petrol arriving ... and took a sample to Mr. Churchill," recalled Clifford Hartley.

By strange twists of fate, the project team were spared much of the scheduled work on the next two major tests planned for the cable. The Luftwaffe and the weather did it for them!

The vulnerability of the cable to bombing or depth-charges obviously had to be put to the test. Hartley had decided to drop a depth-charge in a deliberate effort to damage the line, but the Germans beat him to it. During an air raid on Swansea, a high-explosive bomb fell within 100 feet of the cable - and it survived unscathed. The weather played its part when Hartley decided to test the possibility of repairing the cable in the event of it being dragged by a ship's anchor. Before he had time to carry out this operation, a gale blew up one night in the Bristol Channel, driving an American ship at rest in the Mumbles anchorage over the line and damaging it. HMS *Holdfast* experienced no difficulty in locating the cable, cutting out the damaged section and running in a new length.

It should be added that it had taken some time to link the cause of this apparently inexplicable fracture in the cable to the American vessel in question. Norman Kemp's narrative tells us how it had remained a mystery to the men who had devised the cable until several days after the damage was discovered, "when security officers told them that an American seaman had been heard talking in a Cardiff pub of a strange sea serpent, which had suddenly reared its gigantic coils behind the ship, and profuse quantities of blood had flowed into the sea." The 'blood' was high-octane aviation spirit, coloured red, which was being pumped at the time of the accident. The skipper of the vessel, unaware of the cable's existence - security and secrecy were absolute - had not reported the incident!

Pumping across the Bristol Channel continued day and night for several months in order to prove the reliability of both cable and pumps, and to train the Army (RE and RASC) personnel who would be responsible for the actual operation of the pipe-line in service after D-Day. The pumping commenced at the original design pressure of 750 lb/sq, but was later gradually increased to 1,500 lb/sq, at which level 56,000 gallons of petrol were pumped to Watermouth each day - and delivered by the Petroleum Board to customers in Devon and Cornwall. This was actually more than the region could absorb, and the Board eventually ordered that pumping should be more than halved to a daily level of 25,000 gallons.

The three-inch cable

By this time, a suggestion from Hartley that the diameter of the pipe should be increased from two inches to three in order to provide individual cables with greater capacity - and reduce the number that would need to be laid - was under consideration. A design was drawn up. Apart from the larger bore, the new cable differed from its predecessor in detail only. With the protective armouring of steel tapes, wire, cotton, paper and jute added, the overall diameter was 4.5 inches. Successful tests proved its worth, and Combined Operations eventually decided that manufacture of the two-inch cable should cease altogether in favour of the larger alternative. Work on producing the newly standardised three-inch HAIS cable[2] began in the autumn of 1943.

The requirement now was for much greater manufacturing capacity. Additional cable-making machines were brought into production, both in the United Kingdom and - principally as a safeguard against bomb damage - in the USA as well. Of the 710 nautical miles of HAIS cable that would eventually be built for Operation PLUTO, 140 miles would be contributed by American manufacturers.

In Britain, one of the largest cable-making installations was at the

[2] *Fully described in Appendices*

works of Callender's Cable and Construction Company, where four machines were employed in cable production. An overhead gantry, 45 feet high, 1,600 feet long, and supported by towers every 70 feet, was built to carry cable from the armouring shop to an adjacent deep-water jetty. Coiling sites, 86 feet in diameter, were located between the towers to facilitate continuous manufacture and loading. Similar installations were constructed at the works of several of the other ten British cable-making firms by now working flat out on HAIS production.

Yet, the development of the HAIS cable was only one half of the emerging story of Operation PLUTO.

CABLE
for
OPERATION "PLUTO"

THE PETROL PIPE-LINES THAT MADE V.E. POSSIBLE!

Coiling a length of many miles of H.A.I.S. Cable outside the HENLEY Cable Factory to await shipment.

THE HENLEY STRAIGHT THROUGH LEAD PRESS. The bulk of the petrol supplied through the H.A.I.S. Cable was and is being delivered through lead pipe extruded on the Henley Lead Press.

Never before has the cable-making industry been called upon to undertake such a unique task as was involved in the production of the cable for operation "PLUTO," the petrol pipe-lines that made V.E. possible. The HENLEY Straight Through Lead Press that successfully produced the largest portion of the lead alloy tubing for this cable is also used for sheathing

HENLEY CABLES

W. T. HENLEY'S TELEGRAPH WORKS CO. LTD.
MILTON COURT · WESTCOTT · DORKING · SURREY

It was not until July 1945 that the HAIS cable manufacturers were able to tell the world about their contribution to Operation PLUTO. This Henley advertisement features the 'straight-through' lead press. (GEC)

Chapter 4
1942-43: PIPE AND DRUM

The HAMEL pipe

Developed initially as an insurance against the possible failure of the HAIS cable, the HAMEL flexible steel pipe was the brainchild of H. A. Hammick, Chief Engineer of the Iraq Petroleum Company, and B. J. Ellis, Burmah Oil's Chief Oilfields Engineer, who in 1942 were heading the team dealing with the early development of Operation PLUTO at the Ministry of Fuel and Power's Petroleum Division.

Noting how flexible the cable was in the longer lengths which were starting to appear - in contrast to the extreme stiffness of the short lengths initially manufactured - Hammick and Ellis suggested that steel pipe would be worth considering as an alternative. Both engineers had been impressed with the flexibility of steel pipe in long lengths during its handling in the oilfields, and felt it could probably be bent round a large-diameter wheel without kinking. Flash-welded, it could be manufactured

The giant 'cotton-reel' that was HMS Conundrum I ... on the stocks at Tilbury. (IWM)

The Conundrum after launching into the Thames. (IWM)

to provide any length required. The idea was quickly put to the test.

Using the expertise of steel-makers Stewarts & Lloyds at Corby (aided by Dartford-based J. & E. Hall, and A. I. Welding), Hammick soon proved that ordinary three-inch steel pipe could be bent round a 30-foot diameter wheel and pulled off again relatively straight, minus kinks. While this was certainly encouraging, a big doubt remained: how long could unprotected steel pipe survive under the conditions expected on the bottom of the English Channel? After some deliberation, there was general agreement that the pipe would last for at least six weeks. Bearing in mind the probable scarcity of lead - unlikely to be sufficient for the amount of HAIS cable then envisaged - the estimated lifespan for HAMEL was reckoned long enough to make its further development a worthwhile consideration.

Apparent from the start was that, unlike the cable, the HAMEL pipe could not be heaped in horizontal coils on a cable ship. This would involve a complete twist in each turn while coiling down the pipe, and again when uncoiling it for laying. Ellis's first idea for getting round this was to use a large wheel mounted on the deck of a converted hopper barge and rotated by winches, with the lower part of the wheel protruding into the sea through the hopper doors. The initial trials, in April 1943, successfully employed this system, using low-carbon, mild-steel piping with

33

an internal diameter of three inches, and a steam hopper fitted-out for the purpose by the Director of Naval Construction, and re-christened HMS *Persephone*[1].

Lengths of HAMEL pipe were hand-welded at Portsmouth Dockyard and wound onto *Persephone* from the quayside. The first experimental lay, at Spithead, was trouble-free - "to the admitted astonishment of most of the spectators," according to Clifford Hartley - and the hopper barge was later able to lay a series of HAMEL pipes across the Solent from Lepe, south of the Fawley oil refinery in Hampshire, to Thorness Bay, near Cowes, on the north-west coast of the Isle of Wight. Not only did this provide valuable training and experience, but the pipe-line thus created beneath the Solent - code-named SOLO - formed a crucial link in the network of pipes leading to the cross-Channel pumping stations constructed in the south-east of the Island, and described in Chapter 6.

Enter the *Conundrum*

Ellis, however, had already noted the potential for a highly ingenious development - one that was to give Operation PLUTO its most enduring visual image. Possibly influenced by his keen enthusiasm for sailing, he had conceived the idea of a floating steel drum, resembling a gigantic cotton reel, which could be wound with an almost unlimited quantity of steel pipe, and towed across the Channel while the pipe was uncoiled onto the seabed. It was the perfect answer to a conundrum - and HMS *Conundrum* was the perfect name chosen for this extraordinary 'cone-ended drum.'

Model tests at the National Physical Laboratory provided Ellis with everything he wanted to hear. The drum could be towed at sufficient laying speed without yawing, while the pipe could not only be bent and pulled off straight, it could also be welded with absolute reliability. With HAIS, at this stage, yet to prove its capabilities, and with the likely shortage of lead uppermost in the minds of the project team, the decision was taken to proceed with the production of HAMEL pipe - and the first of the bizarre *Conundrums* - as a matter of priority.

[1] *An appropriate choice - Persephone (or Prosperine) was the mythological wife of Pluto.*

34

The piping itself was made at Corby by Stewarts & Lloyds, and delivered by rail from the East Midlands to the Thames port of Tilbury. The company was also appointed agents of the Petroleum Division for the design, construction and, subsequently, the operation of a purpose-equipped factory (later duplicated by another, built alongside) at Tilbury to weld 40-foot sections of the pipe into 4,000-foot lengths. After welding had taken place, the finished pipe was pushed into conveyor channels of the same length, then automatically thrown off into storage racks at a speed in excess of 100 mph.

From storage it could be wound directly onto the *Conundrum*. The floating drum was held in position by two arms hinged to the end of the winding jetty. During the winding operation, it was rotated and the pipe under tension was drawn up onto the drum and positioned by overhead traversing gear. It was possible to ballast the drum so that, at the start of winding, it was well down in the water. As loading proceeded, and the weight of the drum increased, the ballast water was removed.

The *Conundrum* - a name that was quickly given the universally-

The impressive dimensions of the Conundrum are apparent in this picture
(IWM)

applied short-form of *Conum* - was designed by the Director of Naval Construction's team, who also supervised its construction at Tilbury by Messrs. Orthostyle. The drum had an overall width of 90 feet, with a 40-foot diameter and 60 feet between the flanges at either end. The flanges themselves were 52 feet in diameter, and were fitted with outer teeth, so that the drum could be rotated for winding, while afloat, by a chain-drive mechanism. The drum could carry up to 80 miles of three-inch steel pipe, and weighed 1,600 tons fully laden with the maximum length.

It was built ashore - as were the five sister drums which followed - at the top of a slipway, "down which she slid cautiously into the dock at her launching," recalled Sir Donald Banks, Director-General of the Petroleum Warfare Department, whose role in Operation PLUTO was about to begin in earnest. "How one would have loved to let her roll down incontinently with the biggest splash in the world!"

Chapter 5
1943: REALIGNMENT

The PWD takes over

Co-operation does not necessarily breed co-ordination - and thus it was with Operation PLUTO up until the spring of 1943. Between them, Combined Operations and the Ministry of Fuel and Power's Petroleum Division had achieved a tremendous amount in bringing both HAIS and HAMEL successfully through their full-scale trials in such a short space of time - but there was no clearly defined administrative structure in place, and this had led to some difficulties. The shortcoming was particularly evident during the HAIS cable trials with HMS *Holdfast* in the Bristol Channel. "Much delay and a certain amount of confusion arose through the absence of properly co-ordinated authority," Sir Donald Banks was later to recall in *Flame over Britain*, his superb narrative of petroleum warfare.

Geoffrey Lloyd was aware of the threat this posed to PLUTO. In April 1943, he took the decision to implement a major administrative and operational re-organisation. The first step was to hand over the entire co-ordinating role to the Petroleum Warfare Department.

Sir Donald Banks, the PWD's Director-General, was then charged with the responsibility for defining who should do what. "After some tricky negotiations," he recalled, "it was agreed that a broad division of functions should leave the Navy with the marine responsibility ... and the War Office with general

Sir Donald Banks, acclaimed Director-General of the Petroleum Warfare Department. He was brought into this specialised branch of warfare by Geoffrey Lloyd in July 1942, assuming a co-ordinating role with Operation PLUTO in April 1943. (IWM)

Captain J. F. Hutchings, RN (front row, centre) and Admiralty staff colleagues of Force PLUTO are pictured aboard HMS Latimer in 1944. (IWM)

supply arrangements, in conjunction with the Petroleum Board and Petroleum Division, who together were responsible for the working of the English pipe-line network, while the Army in the Field would run the pipe-lines on the mainland of Europe. The Petroleum Warfare Department, in addition to co-ordinating and progressing the plan generally, were given the responsibility for erecting and controlling the high-power pumping stations on the English shores. Combined Operations, who had originally sponsored the military side of the plan, now stood aside, and it was necessary to find someone to take their place in charge of the sea operations."

The Admiralty soon provided the pipe-line operation with its own speciaised task force - designated Force PLUTO - and the vital gap at the top was filled by Captain J. F. Hutchings, RN, "to become famed (and sometimes defamed!) as S.N.O. PLUTO." wrote Banks. Sir Donald's vivid description of Hutchings, and the role this inspirational officer subsequently played in PLUTO, is well worth repeating:

"He was a typical Naval officer of what I think is known as the 'torpedo school' - hearty, sanguine, full of enthusiasm and abounding in ingenuities, absolutely unconquerable by difficulties, and with a mastery of

38

seamanship that commanded admiration. Through, over, or under one obstacle or another, he blasted, soared or wriggled his way, and the final triumph of the enterprise must be ascribed in no small measure to his indomitable qualities. He collided frequently with the engineers and with the diverse authorities of Supreme Headquarters Allied Expeditionary Force, and of the Admiralty, and he went a freebooter's way through Naval store-keeping. But, as far as I am aware, these collisions were reserved exclusively for those of higher spheres, and he enjoyed a confidence and loyalty amongst the miscellaneous ranks of Force PLUTO, which was not the least of his achievements."

On 24 April 1943 the Quartermaster-General to the Forces, General Sir Thomas Riddell-Webster, personally inspected the HAIS cable in operation at Watermouth Bay. Five days later, he visited the HAMEL factory at Tilbury, and saw HAIS cable in production at Henley's Gravesend factory and at Siemens' in Woolwich. At Siemens, he also watched HMS *Holdfast* loading a length of two-inch HAIS cable, which had yet to be superseded by its three-inch successor. It was the Quartermaster-General's decision, in ordering the further manufacture of HAIS cable, to have the three-inch version - with its capacity almost treble that of its predecessor - thoroughly put to the test. Pipe-line capacity was about to become a priority.

Cherbourg targeted

The political, military and moral arguments over the planned cross-Channel invasion of Hitler's Fortress Europe, vociferously debated by the Allied war leaders and their strategic planners over a long period, had reached virtual deadlock by June 1943. It was the backdrop for Lord Louis Mountbatten's finest hour. Having spent the previous 18 months in full-time study of all aspects of the great invasion, Britain's Chief of Combined Operations was convinced that it could be successfully undertaken. His firm conviction was in no small measure based on the supplies that could be made available to the invasion forces, once ashore, by the use of ingenious novel developments such as the Mulberry artificial harbours and PLUTO. Mountbatten now used his immense personal stand-

One method of delivering completed HAIS cable from factory lines to the waterside for loading onto the cable ship. (IWM)

ing to full effect.

On 28 June he whisked the planners away from London to the comparative peace and clear air of Largs, on the west coast of Scotland, where a Combined Ops. training school was located. In the town's Hollywood Hotel (which served as a Naval shore base), Mountbatten took the leading role in a top-secret, high-security conference code-named RATTLE. At the top of a formidable list of 'guest stars,' the Allied armies were represented by no less than 20 Generals, the air forces by eleven Air Marshals and Commodores, and the naval forces by eight Admirals. Lord Louis and Lieutenant-General Sir Frederick Morgan, Chief of Staff to the Supreme Allied Commander (Designate) - COSSAC for short - somehow succeeded in bringing minds together despite the wide gulf in opinion which had previously existed. At last, the preparations for invasion could progress on a united front.

Major decisions were taken at, and immediately following, the RATTLE Conference - and none were more fundamental than the agreement that was reached on where the landings should take place. Until Largs, there had still been strong support - particularly among some of the British planners - for an invasion zone in the Pas de Calais, a short sea route across the Dover Straits from south-eastern England. This was certainly the crossing envisaged during the early development of PLUTO. For many people, Pas de Calais was the obvious location for the assault. Mountbatten, however, had long opposed it - "resolutely and ceaselessly," to quote his own words - pointing out that it was *too* obvious.

The Germans, he argued, were anticipating just such an attack, and were rapidly building up military strength in considerable depth throughout the Calais area - on the coast and tucked-in behind it - as a countermeasure. They had little of the same motivation further west, and consequently had allocated nothing like the same level of fortifications and military manpower to the defence of the Normandy beaches in the Baie de la Seine, between the Cotentin and Dieppe. The enemy did not expect an attack on Normandy. Mountbatten insisted that this was where it should take place. At Largs, he finally convinced the planners that he was right. Operation Overlord now had Normandy firmly in its sights.

For Operation PLUTO this meant a major new strand of policy. By July 1943 the Quartermaster-General's Petroleum Committee had recom-

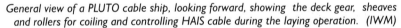

General view of a PLUTO cable ship, looking forward, showing the deck gear, sheaves and rollers for coiling and controlling HAIS cable during the laying operation. (IWM)

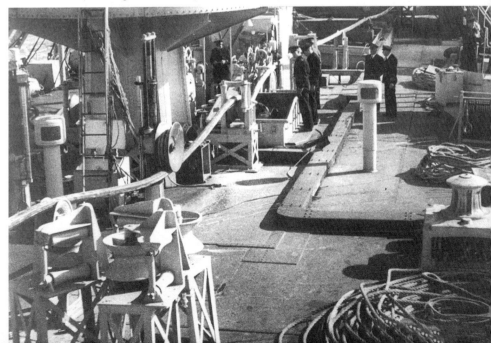

mended that the internal English pipe-line system should be extended to link up with projected cross-Channel PLUTO pumping stations on the Kent coast at Dungeness, and on the Isle of Wight, from where it was now planned - for the first time - to install a PLUTO line to Cherbourg in order to fuel the initial Allied assault on the Normandy beaches. The undersea link would be more than three times the length of the originally envisaged 20 nautical miles, or thereabouts, towards which the development of the pipe-line project had until this point been exclusively geared. Despite this, the Chiefs of Staff Committee confirmed the recommendations. Operation PLUTO was now a bigger animal - and its needs that much greater.

Chapter 6
1943-44: BAMBI AND DUMBO

Sandown and Shanklin selected

Construction work on the Dungeness pumping station - intended for secondary use once the invasion had gained its initial foothold and petrol could be pumped safely across the Straits of Dover - was quickly put in hand. Finding a suitable site for the PLUTO pumps on the Isle of Wight, now very much the number one priority, was a lot more troublesome. Sir Donald Banks and his team had calculated that a pipe-line to Cherbourg from the southern shores of the Island, a distance of some 70 nautical miles, was feasible - but only just. So they searched for a terminal site on Wight as near to France as it was possible to get. "Clambering over the rocky coastline from Dunnose Head to St Catherine's Point, we sought in vain for some suitable sandy cove where we could lay our lines," he recalled.

The tidal currents and jagged reefs in the far south of the Island offered too many hazards. There was no option but to add still further to the length of the line by retreating a few miles northwards to the pre-war

The feeder pipe-line network bringing the oil to the South Coast PLUTO terminals used trestle bridges to cross undulating countryside. (IWM)

holiday beaches of Sandown Bay. Shanklin, the most southerly of the resorts which punctuate the line of the coast in the bay, was now earmarked as departure point for the Cherbourg connection.

Before PLUTO's giant tentacle could be thrown out across the Channel, Shanklin had to be connected to the, by now, well-developed internal pipe-line system in England, in order to receive oil from the tanker ports on the Mersey and in the Bristol Channel. The southernmost pipe-line, heading eastwards from Avonmouth, was joined in 1942 by a spur which ran from Aldermaston, in Berkshire, down to the Hamble oil terminal, east of Southampton, in Hampshire. Force PLUTO carried the line in 1943 across Southampton Water to the shores of the Solent at Lepe, from where the still experimental HAMEL pipe was laid by HMS *Persephone* - as described in chapter 4 - alongside HAIS cable to form the SOLO pipe-line to Thorness Bay, in the north of the Isle of Wight.

From a pumping station at the isolated Whippance Farm, the final, buried, link in the chain was laid across the Island from Thorness, via the thickly-wooded Parkhurst Forest, to a 620,000-gallon reservoir tank built - beneath nearly an acre of camouflage netting - in the small woodland of Hungerberry Copse, situated on high ground just to the west of Shanklin. From the tank - endearingly code-named TOTO - the oil was fed by gravity down forking lines to seafront pumping installations, both at Shanklin

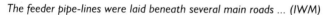

The feeder pipe-lines were laid beneath several main roads ... (IWM)

44

itself and at the neighbouring resort of Sandown, nearly three miles to the north.

"It was part of all the plans," recalled Sir Donald Banks, "to insure and re-insure against enemy action, not only by dispersion and conceal-ment, but by duplicating, so that if one lot of pumps was knocked out, another would take its place. So two (HAMEL) sea-lines were laid by *Persephone* across the bay, connecting-up the two stations laterally."

Shanklin had suffered badly at the hands of the Luftwaffe, particularly from the tip-and-run raiders whose low-level, quick-fire attacks were a terrifying and devastating feature of the mid-war years in the Isle of Wight. As a consequence, several of the hotels and villas which made up the town's Victorian seafront had been reduced to little more than rubble. Residents who had remained in those homes that were left standing were evacuated and required to live either in the town above or with relatives elsewhere, and for a time the Esplanade was used to train soldiers in the techniques of house-to-house fighting. Thus scarred by friendly and enemy forces, Shanklin's seafront was a pathetic sight - unless you hap-pened to be looking for somewhere to conceal massive pumps for an oil pipe-line across the Channel. Just as they had done at Swansea, during the HAIS cable trials, the Luftwaffe unwittingly provided a helping hand for Operation PLUTO at Shanklin.

Among the shattered remains of the Esplanade - principally amid the ruins of the Royal Spa Hotel, near the town's cliff lift - hidden pump-houses were built and pipe-lines laid. Sir Donald has described the lengths to which his team worked to conceal it all from the enemy in the sky, "simulating on a new elevation - twelve feet higher up the debris and wrecked dwelling-rooms - even the contents of the bathrooms, that strewed the ground, and hiding our mechanisms beneath this false floor." From the cliff lift, the pipe-line run along the gutter of the Esplanade as far as the town's pier, which - like most seaside piers in wartime England - had lost its centre section as a precaution against the feared invasion. The pipe-line was laid down the pier and, forking into two, crossed the gap in the form of a suspension bridge. This was equipped with flat treads, handrails and a notice warning military personnel to walk out of step if they crossed the 'bridge' more than two at a time - to prevent setting the structure in motion! From here, the pipe- line was fed over the pier landing-stage and into the sea.[1]

Sandown had not suffered air raid damage on the same scale as its neighbour, but here there was no need for bombed-out hotels to conceal the presence of PLUTO. At the north end of the resort's long seafront, in the area of Yaverland, stood a redundant, partly-demolished granite fort, built at an earlier time of conflict to defend the Island against a possible invasion by the forces of Napoleon III. The thick casements of the fort's old gun emplacements provided almost perfectly secure hideaways for the pumping machinery. "We installed enough ... to keep some ten to 15 Army divisions supplied with motor spirit," Banks recalled.[2]

The original plans for the PLUTO pumping stations had made provision for batteries of diesel-driven reciprocating pumps, which had consequently been ordered in large numbers. The subsequent decision to invade Normandy, and lay the long pipe-line to Cherbourg, greatly increased the pumping capacity required. As a result, large centrifugal pumps, electrically-driven from the grid, were also installed, one consequence being a reduction in the number of staff needed for both operation and maintenance. While both Isle of Wight pumping stations were equipped with two centrifugal pumps, each with a daily capacity of 330,000 gallons, Sandown had twice as many reciprocating pumps - 16 against Shanklin's eight - each with a daily capacity of 36,000 gallons. All the pumps delivered at a pressure of 1,500 lb/sq.

Together, Sandown and Shanklin constituted the primary PLUTO pumping station in England at that time, and were collectively endowed with another delightfully incongruous Disney-esque code-name - BAMBI. There was, however, no acronym at work here. BAMBI just happened to be lying around at the time! "We found him in grown-up antlers, a full-fledged stag's head, amid the rubble of a bombed villa, and he became henceforth a mascot for the Pioneers and the men of the Royal Army

[1] *Shanklin Pier was destroyed by the hurricane which hit the Isle of Wight in 1987.*
[2] *The old fort now houses the Isle of Wight Zoo.*

46

... and sometimes under railway lines. (IWM)

Service Corps, and of my devoted staff who laboured long hours through the winter of 1943 to have him ready for the fray when the boats were launched for the further shore," recalled Sir Donald Banks in his book.

Pioneers' recollections

Among the men of the Pioneer Corps involved with the BAMBI project were Sergeants Reg Parker and Ben Scothen, both of No. 13 Company. Their joint recollections make fascinating reading:

"In September 1943, 13 Company was ordered to a secret destination, and speculation ran rife! After a journey filled with apprehension and visions of troopships and the Middle East, we eventually arrived at Sandown, Isle of Wight - there to take up residence in the most palatial hotel that the resort afforded, instead of our visualised dug-outs of the Eastern deserts! On our first day, at a security lecture and film show, the nature of our job was given to all - soldiers and a scattering of civilians alike - who were to take part in launching this gigantic project, that was to be known to the world - some months later - as Operation PLUTO. In the interests of security, the unit designation was discarded and 13 Company Pioneer Corps became known as 'A' Company, HQ 311 Infantry Brigade. A closed address was used and unit censorship was immediately instituted. Leave was cancelled, and the taking of pictures was strictly forbidden. The project headquarters for both military and civilian personnel was the Grand Hotel.

"PLUTO (a name we had yet to hear) was commenced in earnest in the

47

dark hours of the following morning - for we eventually worked from dawn to dusk. In brief, our task at Sandown and Shanklin was to prepare, build and install the large engines, pumps and shore pipe-line at both sites. Mention must be made of the wonderful camouflage ... which was supervised by Lieut. MacPherson, RE. An example of this was the setting of grass seed on the roofs of the pump-houses, the seed having to be watered and cared for daily - as if it were the lawn of a well-run household! Camouflage, to us Pioneers, was a source of great annoyance, arguments, cursing and extra work, but as the days passed, and after the attempted bombings of Jerry had failed at both sites, we fully realised the importance of first-class camouflage. This first part of our task completed, we were granted a brief respite, in the shape of training, for the expected and much-awaited 'great day' ..."

Reg Langstaff, another of the Pioneer Corps' September 1943 arrivals at Sandown - after being stationed for three years at Swindon - recalled being billeted with his Company at the Ocean Hotel, and shortly afterwards starting work on PLUTO. "But the project was so secret that quite a few weeks passed before we knew what was going on. Our Company was, more or less, split in two, with approximately half the men working behind the granite fort at Sandown, and in some of the buildings of Brown's golf course alongside, where huge pumps were housed.

"The other half were at Shanklin, where a huge concrete-mixer was installed inside the ruins of the Royal Spa Hotel. Each time a lorry entered the building to load up with concrete etc., the doors were immediately closed behind it. The same thing happened after it left to take the load along the seafront, and then behind the hotels, where buildings were erected to house the pumps. Some men were detailed to brush out the tyre marks which were made each time a lorry went along the front - in case enemy aircraft came over to take photographs. Everything had to be maintained as if nothing was taking place. I remember the workings of Shanklin Cliff Lift were removed to make way for the project, and I guess there may have been a shortage of timber during that period because we were detailed to strip quite a few of the hotels along the front of all their timbered floors. The wood was then used to shore-up the solid concrete 'bed' inside the buildings which had been put up behind the hotels. Once all the floors in the hotels had been removed, you could see the sky through those parts of the roof where the slates were missing, as you looked up from the bare ground below."

Developing Dungeness

Dungeness was the haunt of DUMBO. Just why the secondary pumping station in Kent should have been given this particular code-name - after yet another animated creation from the Disney studio - is still a matter for some conjecture, though the first two letters need little explanation. Banks suggests it was because the station, "like its namesake with the stumbling gait and big flopping ears," sprawled all over the shingle-strewn wastes of the Dungeness promontory. It was fed by oil from the West Coast tanker ports via an eastwards extension of the pipe-line linking Avonmouth with Walton-on-Thames, in Surrey, and also by a supplementary spur pipe from the Isle of Grain oil terminal, between the mouths of the Thames and Medway rivers in the north of Kent.

With Dungeness within range of the German guns at Gris Nez, subterfuge was used to good effect at DUMBO, too. The route of the pipe-line in its final stages deliberately gave the impression that the eventual destination was the coastal area between Hythe and Folkestone, further up the Kent coast. If located by the enemy, this would suggest a convenient location for fuelling an invasion across the nearby Straits of Dover - rather

A raised section of feeder pipe-line near the BAMBI pumping terminal at Shanklin, Isle of Wight. (IWM)

than the now formally adopted Normandy assault plan.

The masses of shingle at Dungeness were used to good effect, helping to hide the pipe-line from view as it neared the pumping stations, spread out along the coastline. The camouflage team, under Captain Ashley Havinden, really came into their own here, concealing the pump installations in the front and back rooms of small seaside villas and bungalows. "Behind the unchanged, smiling facades of 'Mon Repos,' 'Happy-Go-Lucky,' 'Sea Breezes.' 'Sans Souci' and a host of others were massive pumps and engines, and the owners would indeed have been surprised had they been able to walk into their erstwhile carefree resorts," wrote Sir Donald Banks.

The effectiveness of the camouflage was tested each week by aerial photography, courtesy of the RAF, and no changes were ever visible. Both at Dungeness and on the Isle of Wight, all plant which might conceivably have been seen from the air was moved into position at night. "Unlike many war secrets," said Clifford Hartley in 1945, "PLUTO could have been given away by a single sentence - for instance: 'A petrol pipe like a hollow submarine cable across the Channel' - and pumping stations and both types of sea lines could easily have been attacked. The complete success of all the precautions, often expensive and irksome, was proved by the lack of any known attempt by the enemy to interfere at any time."

Dungeness was eventually equipped with 30 reciprocating and four centrifugal pumps, divided between its three well-dispersed coastal sites. Both here and on the Isle of Wight, the terminals were built under the supervision of Anglo-Iranian Oil, using civilian contractors and men from units of the Royal Engineers, the Royal Army Service Corps (represented by its own Bulk Petroleum Company) and the Pioneer Corps, who were being trained in specific areas of their operation.

Thus, the landward preparation for Operation PLUTO, inarguably one of the best-kept secrets of the build-up to D-Day, advanced towards the crucial operational stage.

Chapter 7
1943-44: A FORCE REINFORCED

The twin need

The decision in July 1943 to link the Isle of Wight and Cherbourg by a 70-mile PLUTO connection created an urgent twin-pronged need at sea. There was now a requirement for cable ships substantially larger than those at first envisaged for the task of laying the cross-Channel HAIS lines. Coupled with that was the need to speed development of the *Conundrums*, which it was now recognised would have to operate heavily overloaded - in fact, so far down on the water that their axles would be completely awash - if they were to carry sufficient HAMEL pipe to make the long lay now demanded. The first was achieved rather more easily than the second.

Captain Hutchings was able to add three more ships to his cable-laying fleet, HMS *Algerian* was a 20-year-old requisitioned merchant ship of 2.300 tons, operated by Ellerman Lines in peacetime, which, while modest, was still substantially larger than the 1,500-ton *Holdfast* used in the early cable-laying trials. The other two additions were a different proposition altogether. HMS *Latimer* and HMS *Sancroft* had been built for the Ministry of War Transport in 1941 and had virtually identical tonnages of around 7,000 tons. While the *Algerian* was converted to carry 30 miles of three-inch cable, the two larger ships both emerged from their conversions with a cable-carrying capacity of 100 miles. In the main, they were crewed - as the *Holdfast* had been - by a mixture of cable hands and merchant seamen. However, because their duties had to be interwoven with naval and military operations, they each flew the White Ensign of the Senior Service - a move which led to much raising of eyebrows at the Admiralty!

To these major acquisitions for Force PLUTO were added a further five

Thames barges, equipped for laying the cable shore-ends, together with a large number of auxiliary vessels. Force headquarters was at Southampton, with a secondary base at Tilbury.

The first *Conundrum* lived up its name when it was put to the test with 70 miles of HAMEL pipe wrapped around its giant spindle in no less than 17 layers. Thus loaded, the *Conum* weighed an impressive 1,600 tons - the equivalent of a naval destroyer! Towing it was going to be a mighty problem. The Admiralty turned out the Ocean Rescue Tug HMS *Bustler*, the most powerful available, for a test run, and there was some dismay when it failed to move the drum at more than three knots. Most of the Royal Navy's largest tugs were already earmarked for other invasion tasks - notably the movement of the giant sections of Mulberry harbour - but Force PLUTO did manage to secure the services of HMS *Marauder* as a partner for the *Bustler*. It made little difference. Together, the tugs raised the towing speed to around four knots. It was not going to be enough to combat the tides in the Channel.

The problem was handed back to the National Physical Laboratory for further model tests, but there was no ready answer. "All solutions failed," recalled Sir Donald Banks, "until a landlubber diffidently suggested that possibly the wake of the tugs impinging on the drum was thrusting it back in proportion to the power employed. The idea at first was ridiculed by the seamen, but eventually they were persuaded to try the expedient of spacing out the tugs so that the wake flowed past, outside the drum. Six or seven knots were then obtained - and the crisis was past." To aid steering, it was decided that a smaller tug should travel astern of the drum.

Trials and tribulations

The full-scale tests for HMS *Conundrum* referred to by Sir Donald began in the Thames during February 1944. In March, she was towed out of the river, down the Kent coast, through the Straits of Dover - remarkably, without attracting the attention of the enemy on the far shore - and along the South Coast as far as Bournemouth Bay, code-named TWEE-DLEDUM for the trials that took place there in April. It was off Bournemouth that *Conundrum I* was operated for the first time at speeds of up to seven knots, successfully laying a loop of some twelve miles of HAMEL pipe. Again, we are indebted to Sir Donald Banks for an evocative eye-witness account of a memorable event in the development of PLUTO:

"It was a lovely sunny day, and the sight of the drum ploughing through the water like some fantastic sea monster, throwing up clouds of white spray in its rotation, was unforgettable. The ends were joined up to the shore, and oil pumped through with complete success. Hammick was a happy man that day, and the stage was now rapidly being set for D-Day."

Yet, there were other problems to overcome - the American involvement for one. As recounted earlier, manufacturers in the USA eventually helped significantly with the production of HAIS cable, but this vital co-operation was not achieved without difficulty. The Americans had themselves been working on an undersea pipe-line, experimenting with a six-inch steel pipe worked at very high (3,000 lb/sq) pressure, and using an intricate radar device to locate the pipe-ends on the seabed, enabling a diver to go down and join them up with flexible joints. While clever, it was considered by its detractors to be over-elaborate and clumsy when compared with HAIS and HAMEL. One distinct disadvantage was the hazards it posed to the divers, who would have to work in tricky tidal con-

Commander Heale (front row, centre) and fellow officers aboard HMS Latimer. Standing (from left): Gunnery Officer, 1st Watchkeeping Officer, 2nd Watchkeeping Officer, Navigating Officer, 2nd Engineering Officer, 1st Signals Officer, 5th Engineering Officer, 2nd Signals Officer (Jim Reeves, who has provided details for this caption), 3rd Engineering Officer. Seated either side of Cddr. Heale are the 1st Lieutenant (left) and Chief Engineer. The 4th Engineering Officer was on leave. (IWM)

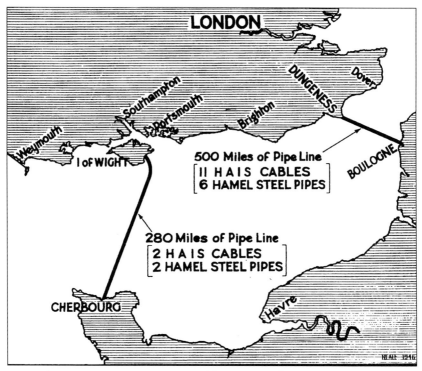

The two cross-Channel PLUTO routes. (GEC)

ditions. Eventually, after US Service Chiefs had attended several of the British pipe-line trials, General Eisenhower, the Allied Supreme Commander, confirmed their decision to adopt PLUTO instead.

This probably didn't help Clifford Hartley, by now the Petroleum Warfare Department's Technical Director, when he visited the USA in February 1944 to seek American cable production assistance. He initially ran into considerable opposition from the manufacturers, and it was only after the intervention of Lucius D. Clay, USA Quartermaster-General, that the necessary machinery for turning out HAIS cable was installed on that side of the Atlantic to allow production to proceed. Pumping and auxiliary plant was also supplied by the Americans to PLUTO once Eisenhower came down in favour of the British scheme.

That period of US involvement is recalled by Ronald Crabtree, who was a member of the first stores department set up in 1942 by the Royal Engineers in the USA to deal with engineering equipment purchased by Britain under the Lend-Lease arrangements, which had been signed in March 1941 with the Americans. "From September 1943 to November 1944 I was liaison officer at the USASF depot in Belle Mead, New Jersey," he remembered. "During that time I was responsible for the marking and shipment of RE stores to the New York seaboard, earmarked for various theatres of war. The most important shipment, which I conveyed to New York overnight, was the 48 gate-valves and associated parts for two high-pressure PLUTO pumping stations. Pictures of the gate-valves being unloaded in France were subsequently published in Washington DC newspapers."

With pumping stations in place, the fleet secured and converted for service, cable and pipe manufacture assured, personnel (around 100 officers and ten times that many men in the task force alone) trained, and trials successfully completed, Operation PLUTO was - according to Hartley's own recollections - ready to run "some weeks before D-Day." In the event, it did not 'run' until some weeks *after* the invasion - and that crucial delay to the Cherbourg connection has marked it down as a failure in the eyes of some commentators in the years that have followed.

Chapter 8
1944: THE 12 DAYS OF BAMBI

PLUTO delayed

The BAMBI pumping installations on the Isle of Wight were inspected by Sir Donald Banks, senior Army officers and the Under-Secretary for War, Sir Eric Speed, on 4 June 1944 as part of a general tour of coastal defences on the Island - an exercise which gave every appearance of a routine inspection despite the high-ranking composition of the party. Sir Donald recalled how Speed "had given out that he was having a picnic lunch there, and was seizing an opportunity to see some of the beauty spots as 'things were fairly quiet.' Never once ... was any reference made to the preparations which were reaching their climax around us." It was a classic example of the great invasion bluff - fooling the enemy into a false sense of security over the date and, just as crucially, the area chosen for the landings. D-Day caught the German defenders in Normandy napping less than 48 hours later.

The first reserves of fuel - 180,000 tons 'packaged' in a vast bank of four-gallon jerricans - had been prepared over a period of several months for carriage across the Channel in the small prefabricated Chant tankers. On D-Day itself, 13,400 tons was transported in this way to the invasion beaches targeted by the British - seven days' supply, at an estimated daily consumption rate of 2,000 tons, for the troops who initially went ashore. That consumption figure rose to 3,000 tons by 1 August, to 5,000 tons by 1 November, and eventually to a peak of 7,000 tons a day by the spring of 1945. The Americans packed the same amount of fuel as the British at the beginning of the assault, but their daily consumption eventually rose to double that of their allies - by which time they were able to rely on bulk supplies shipped direct from the United States by tanker.

Operation PLUTO was to have entered the fray 18 days after D-Day

(24 June), when the first pipe-line was scheduled for laying from Cherbourg to the Isle of Wight. By D+75 (20 August), the whole of the envisaged system from BAMBI was due to have been in place across the Channel. The reality was somewhat different.

By 3 July oil from England *was* running through underwater pipes onto a Normandy beach - but these were not the lines from Sandown Bay. Midway between GOLD and OMAHA invasion beaches, the small fishing port of Port-en-Bessin, north-west of Caen, had been an early capture for the 47th Royal Marine Commandos. It had been chosen for the initial reception of oil in bulk - as opposed to the 'packed' supplies - which were shipped across the Channel in ocean-going tankers. Moored off the open beach, the vessels discharged their contents for pumping ashore through the ship-to-shore pipe-lines code-named TOMBOLA. While they waited for their cross-Channel link to enter service, it was the men of Force PLUTO who laid the first TOMBOLA line on 25 June. Two lines were eventually put down at Port-en-Bessin for the use of the British, and another five were laid for the American forces at St Honorine des Pertes, a few miles to the west. Yet, the TOMBOLA pipe-lines tended to break, and were only a limited success.

HMS Latimer is pictured during her historic first cable-laying run from Shanklin to Cherbourg on 10 August 1944. (IWM)

The end of the line. Although taken at Boulogne, this view is typical of the PLUTO shore terminals. (IWM)

But why was PLUTO itself now so far behind schedule? The principal reason was the time it took for Cherbourg to fall into Allied hands. The Americans finally wrested it from the Germans during the last days of June, but the final battles for the port left it a shambles - and there was a further major obstacle to overcome before it could be made safe for Allied use. Cherbourg's defenders had left both port and harbour heavily and ingeniously mined. This led to protracted discussion, lasting a full month, over the siting of the pipe-line terminal. Should it be located outside the breakwater, which could make the discharge of oil that much more difficult, or inside it, which might endanger the harbour? Eventually, it was decided to run the pipe-line to a terminal which was outside the harbour altogether - at the sandy bay of Urville-Nacqueville, to the west of Cherbourg. Disney was deserted this time - the code-name for Nacqueville was WATSON![1]

The first lay

It was not until 10 August that HMS *Latimer* was finally able to set out for France and, two days later, embark on the first PLUTO lay from Nacqueville to Sandown Bay. The operation on 12 August was blessed with fine weather and calm sea conditions. Protected from above by fighter planes, and at sea by an escort of Royal Navy patrol vessels, an

---

[1] *Sometimes refered to as BAMBI FAR*

58

unhindered *Latimer* efficiently laid the first HAIS line in ten hours before coming to anchor off Shanklin Pier. With cable ship and escorts safely moored in the bay, preparations were being made to bring the cable ashore. But then a message in semaphore from one of the Royal Navy patrol vessels literally spelt disaster. Her anchor had caught the cable on the seabed, and wrenched it up in what Banks later called "a hopeless snarl." It was a bitter disappointment.

Two days later, HMS *Sancroft* left Force PLUTO's Southampton base[2] for the Cotentin. Again, the cable-lay on her return run to Sandown Bay was successfully completed - and again there were problems in bringing the cable ashore. In attempting to effect this, HMS *Algerian* got a warp around her propeller, and another cable-lay was aborted in its final stage. There was no doubt that the laying operation itself had been mastered, but the shore-end connection continued to plague Operation PLUTO for same time to come. There was also a recurrent problem with undersea leaks in the cable relatively close to the shore, which were a direct result of those failed attempts at shore-end connection. Various liquids were pumped from BAMBI in a bid to pinpoint the leaks - with aircraft flying overhead to spot the resultant patches on the surface of the water.

Since the art of connecting-up the pipe to the shore had been fully mastered in the Bristol Channel and Solent trials, the failure in Sandown Bay has generally been put down to insufficient training of the naval laying party involved in this early operational stage of PLUTO. Whatever the underlying reasons, it was not until 18 September that a HAIS line was connected-up to the shore and successfully water-tested. Four days later petrol at last started to flow through the cable. Delivered at a daily rate of 56,000 gallons, it was forced through at a pumping pressure of 750 lb/sq. The delays and teething troubles could now be submerged - for the time being - by a sense of achievement. Operation PLUTO was up and running.

General Riddell-Webster saw fit at this juncture to recall the mythological origins of the name. "Well done, the King of the Underworld," he told Banks in a telegram from Scotland.

[2] *At the Supermarine works, Woolston.*

The cross-Channel cable from the laying vessel - here beached in Cherbourg Harbour - ran across the beach for connecting to the shore-end sections and the overland pipe-line network beyond. (IWM)

But what of the HAMEL pipe? Laying such a long line from the heavily-laden *Conundrums* was always going to be a tricky operation - especially when faced with the fast-moving tides racing past the rock-strewn seabed of the Cotentin peninsular. And so it proved. HMS *Conundrum I* tried first, on 27 August, but was pulled out of the task before even reaching France. According to Sir Donald, "some ten tons of barnacles from Southampton Water had joined *Conundrum I* during the interval when she was an anchor there, no doubt with laudable intentions to take part in the invasion. But their unauthorised attachment upset the balance of things, and we had to try again." Luck continued to desert the operation on the second and third attempts with the drum, the HAMEL pipe breaking on the latter run nearly 30 miles out from Cherbourg, an incident generally thought to be the result of it fouling and being ripped open on the drum's sharp flanges.

The rise and fall

Then, on 29 September, *Conundrum II* made up for the earlier disappointments by running trouble-free, despite a choppy sea, from Nacqueville and delivering the pipe safely ashore in Sandown Bay.

Pumping tests with water began shortly afterwards - and then petrol was flowing through steel pipe as well as cable. "We were cock-a-whoop at the success of the twin enterprises," wrote Banks.

While most sources - official and otherwise - refer to their being two lines of HAIS cable and two of HAMEL pipe between BAMBI and WAT-SON, it seems likely that only one of each was ever successfully connected and used. The narrative of Sir Donald Banks' certainly indicates that this was the case, particularly his reference to the events of early October which - along with the fast changing military requirements across the Channel - precipitated the end of the BAMBI operation less than a

Sappers from the Royal Engineers are pictured assembling high-pressure pumps at the main arterial pumping station at Cherbourg. (IWM)

fortnight after its delayed commissioning on 22 September.

"On October 3rd," Sir Donald recalled, "the elation was soon changed to funereal gloom when it had been decided to increase the pressure on the HAIS cable. It climbed steadily without incident to over 1,000 lb per square inch, when suddenly. in the middle of the night, the indicators went wild and dropped to next-to-nothing. Our precious cable had gone. Later, on the shorter crossing (from Dungeness), pressures of 1,200 lb/sq were achieved without any trouble at all, and in subsequent investigations it emerged clearly that the trouble was at the coupling, where no doubt it could have been remedied." Worse was to follow. "Later the same night, the duty officer reported that the HAMEL also had failed, probably breaking across a sharp edge on the sea bottom. Our cup of woe was full indeed."

No repairs were attempted. The rapid advance of the Allied armies along the French coast, and the capture of the deep-water facilities at Le Havre as well as those at Cherbourg, had dramatically altered the fuel supply requirements. A developing pipe-line network from Port-en-Bessin had been linked-up with Cherbourg, where tankers direct from the USA were now discharging, and speedily extended by US Engineers south-eastwards, via Chartres, to run south of Paris *en route* to the German frontier. A spur pipe branched out from Port-en-Bessin to reach the Lower Seine at Rouen. Rather than extending this further to the east, a much better option for fuelling the military advance was clearly apparent. Attention was now focussed on the Straits of Dover - and the shorter PLUTO link from Dungeness. On 4 October, the cross-Channel flow of petrol from the BAMBI pumping site at Sandown Bay to Nacqueville was wound-up. It had lasted just 12 days.

Chapter 9
1944-45: DUMBO TAKES CHARGE

Laying to Boulogne

The original site chosen for the PLUTO terminal at Boulogne was the beach at Ambleteuse. When, after capture of the port, this was found to be heavily mined, the decision was taken to terminate the pipe-line instead at a beach within the outer harbour of Boulogne itself. This meant a longer run for Captain Hutchings and his pipe-laying fleet than had been envisaged, and difficult operating conditions in the approaches to the port - not helped by the fact that they, too, were heavily populated with mines. Once these were cleared, Hutchings wasted no time in getting the laying operation under way. HMS *Sancroft* managed an incident-free first run on 10 October with the HAIS cable - but, as with so many of the earlier runs into Sandown Bay, problems were encountered bringing in the shore end at Dungeness.

A revised method of shore-end connection had been adopted in the light of the experience gained off the Isle of Wight. The main cross-Channel cable, paid out over the stern of the cable ship, was dropped from the vessel at either end of the run and marked by a buoy. At low tide, it was recovered and connected to the shore-end cable, ready-coiled in a Thames barge - which then laid it at high water. The end of this section was dropped above the low-water mark, ready for connecting to the pump delivery lines, at the English end, and the tank lines, at the other.

However, Dungeness was not the ideal reception point for this ingenious operation. "The shallow beach made it difficult for the Navy to deliver the cable to high-water mark - their appointed limit," recalled Sir Donald Banks. "Lieut-Colonel Danger's men of the Royal Army Service Corps, who were responsible for the manning of the pumps both at DUMBO and BAMBI, stood for hours up to their wastes in the chilly seawater easing the heavy length ashore - and made a fine job of it."[1]

This set the pattern for the following days. The crews of *Sancroft* and *Latimer* experienced little difficulty in successively laying cable, despite fairly rough seas on occasions, but the operation invariably ended with a protracted and troublesome coupling of the main cable to the shore-ends. However, the RASC contingent at DUMBO stuck to their task manfully, and eventually mastered the technique. At DUMBO FAR - as the terminal at Boulogne was code-named - the main cable was dropped and buoyed by the cable-layer outside the harbour mouth, and run ashore from there, using the method described. The shore-end operation here was under the guidance of Captain H. B. Eagle, RNR, whose unique experience with sea pipe-lines off the oilfields of Sarawak was used to good effect.

But, largely because of deteriorating weather, the start of pumping from DUMBO was delayed until 27 October. "There were frequent changes of plan, and the enthusiasm of the PLUTO force gradually dwindled," wrote D. J. Payton-Smith in his 1971 study of wartime oil policy and administration - a markedly less enthusiastic appraisal of PLUTO than that provided by Sir Donald Banks. "By the middle of December, only six HAIS cables were in position, of which only four were actually working. Their performance was disappointing. It had been planned to pump oil through them at a pressure of 1,500 lb/sq, but, in fact, owing to the way they had been laid, pressure had to be kept down to 350-440 lb. Daily deliveries across the Channel amounted to no more than 700 tons. During 85 days down to 20 January 1945, only 62,000 tons of oil, all of it petrol (for the original plan to pump aviation spirit as well was never implemented) was pumped through DUMBO."

This downbeat assessment was clearly shared by senior Navy officials at the time. In December 1944, the Admiralty had raised the question of whether PLUTO was worth continuing with, in view of the number of ships and men involved in it. "By then," added Payton-Smith, "Antwerp, although under heavy bombardment from flying-bombs and rockets, was

[1] *Apart from manning the pumps - on both sides of the Channel - the RASC's terminal responsibilities also included operating control rooms and storage facilities.*

64

receiving one ocean tanker a day; and small tankers were carrying some 2,500-3,000 tons a day to Ostend, and comparable quantities to Le Havre. The matter was considered by the Joint Administrative Planning Staff. The strongest argument for continuing with PLUTO was the need to save small tankers, which were wanted for service in the Far East. Only Cherbourg and Antwerp could take ocean tankers, and it was not possible to step up supplies through these ports. Accordingly, on 2 January 1945, the Principal Administrative Officers Committee ruled that DUMBO should continue.

"The intention was to use up all the HAIS cable to achieve an estimated 3,300 tons a day through the system by 1 February (allowing for a reserve capacity of 50 per cent, which was thought essential) and assuming that more careful laying would allow the oil to be pumped under the planned pressure of 1,500 lb/sq. No plans were made for using the HAMEL pipe since it had not yet proved possible to lay this successfully, even under summer conditions."

While the implementation of PLUTO is awaited, fuel for the Allied troops is pumped from tankers into a pipe-line laid along a jetty in France. (IWM)

On the last point, Payton-Smith is certainly at variance with Banks, who recalled that the start of the HAMEL pipe-laying operation between Dungeness and Boulogne coincided with a change for the worse in the autumn weather. "Conditions were so variable ... that it was essential to cut to a minimum the time of the whole operation, from setting out from the Thames estuary to the final run off the reel of the French coast," he wrote. The weather posed problems for the *Conundrums*. Despite their extraordinary appearance, they rode the sea well under tow, irrespective of conditions, but were difficult to anchor off a lee shore. Caught in a heavy wind while being moored off Dungeness, one of the drums careered out of control onto the shore, finishing up a total wreck, "amid a gigantic welter of unravelled steel pipes," according to Sir Donald's graphic description. Fortunately, this was to prove an isolated incident - but pulling the pipe ashore from the drums was a persistent problem.

The HAIS-HAMEL connection

"The solution was found by winding turns of HAIS cable on the *Conum* at the beginning and end of each length of HAMEL, followed by a special floating wire," Clifford Hartley later recalled. "With that arrangement, the handling of the shore-end of the *Conum* pipe-line was similar to that of the HAIS cable laid from the cable ships." This technique, known as the HAIS-HAMEL system, was commissioned in January 1945 at

A corner of the main PLUTO control room at Dungeness. An RASC officer stands by a valve control panel, 24 feet long, and adjusts one of the 376 coloured discs marking the locations of the main operating valves, and indicating whether they are open or closed. (IWM)

Boulogne. Here, the drum was towed right into the harbour and moored alongside a jetty, where the pipe was cut and drawn off, as described. Subsequently, the system was developed in a HAIS-HAMEL-HAIS combination, allowing use of the flexible cable at both ends of the cross-Channel line. Having had the news of a successful HAMEL lay in January reported to them, the Principal Administrative Officers Committee, meeting in the middle of February, authorised the laying of five further lines of the steel pipe - in addition to the HAIS cable - in order to achieve the maximum saving of small tankers.

At Boulogne, the pipe-lines were brought ashore near the Hotel Imperial, on the town's seafront, where a valve manifold system and storage tank were installed to provide test facilities.[2] From here, the fuel was pumped uphill, through three lines of six-inch jointed pipe, to the 1,200-ton main storage tanks and pumping installations near Fort de la Creche, to the north of the town. Connections were made here with the overland pipe-line, also of six-inch diameter, which ran to Calais - and eventually for some 200 miles through Belgium and Holland to cross the German border.[3]

In all, 17 pipe-lines were laid between Dungeness and Boulogne - eleven of them a mixture of three-inch and two-inch HAIS cable, and the remainder, HAMEL pipe - up until the German surrender in May 1945.[4] Indeed, the last three-inch HAIS cable was actually laid on 24 May, more than two weeks *after* the Nazi capitulation - since it was the quickest way of clearing the cable ship on which it was wound. Of the 17 lines, a maximum of eleven were probably usable at any one time, allowing a total throughput capacity of more than 4,500 tons (1,350,000 gallons) a day. As for actual performance, Clifford Hartley has recorded that a throughput rate of a million gallons a day was achieved "for some time." The DUMBO system remained in use until the end of July, moving petrol originally pumped from the War Office storage on the Isle of Grain. Then, in

[2] *The Hotel Imperial had served as a Rear GHQ for the British Expeditionary Force before before the retreat from Dunkirk in May 1940.*
[3] *See following chapter and Appendix 8.*
[4] *Payton-Smith differs from most sources by referring to 16 lines from DUMBO, rather than 17.*

One of the giant steel Conundrums in distinctive pipe-laying action in the English Channel. (IWM)

order to release technical manpower, the cross-Channel pipe-line was abandoned, and the fuel supplies it had been carrying were routed, via tankers, through Antwerp.

Apart from problems associated with coupling difficulties, the HAIS cable, once laid, proved an outstanding engineering success on the Boulogne route. Not a single major defect was recorded throughout its period of operation. The HAMEL pipe's short life expectancy of six weeks was achieved by all six of the lines laid - in fact they did rather better than that. Sir Donald Banks recorded that the steel lines "cut through on the reefs near Bassure-de-Baas successively in 77, 52, 55, 112, 55 and 60 days."

Chapter 10
1944-45: BEYOND PLUTO

Pipes into Germany

Beyond PLUTO on the European mainland was the military pipe-line network - referred to in the previous chapter - which progressed quickly along two major routes behind the Allied armies as they advanced across the Continent. The longest, the southern pipe-line from Port-en-Bessin and Cherbourg, eventually reached Mainz, not far short of Frankfurt am Main, in Germany, a distance of some 500 miles, after its journey south of Paris via Alençon, Chartres and Chalon-sur-Saône. The northern system, from Boulogne and Calais, headed for the Low Countries, passing through Ghent, where large tankage installations were helpfully left behind by the retreating Germans (and where a spur line branched off to Ostend) to skirt Antwerp - joined by its own spur to the main line - and then split into two. One fork headed into Holland to supply the British forces through Eindhoven and Emmerich, on the German border, while the other transported fuel to the Americans via Maastricht and, eventually, the German town of Wesel.

Though it was linked to, and effectively extended, the incoming PLUTO lines at Cherbourg and Boulogne - thus providing a continuous pipe-line connection all the way from the Mersey to the Rhine - the military pipe-line network on the Continent was distinct from the specialised cross-Channel links - as was the bulk of the internal pipe-line system in England. On land, Operation PLUTO 'proper' was confined to the lines purpose-built to the two English terminals - between Hamble, Fawley, Thorness and Sandown Bay in the case of BAMBI; between Walton-on-Thames and Dungeness, plus the spur to the Isle of Grain, in the case of DUMBO - and the short connections between the shore terminals and the military pipe-lines in France. PLUTO was part of the network - rather

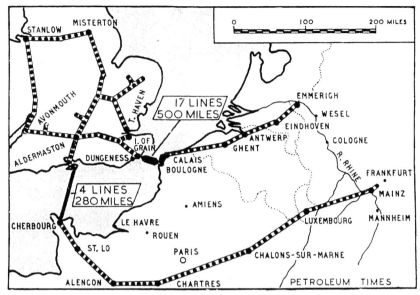

The main network of English and Continental pipe-lines, linked across the Channel by
PLUTO. Published in the Petroleum Times on 9 June 1945, this was the first diagram of
the network to be made public. Secondary lines were omitted. (GEC)

than the other way round.

However, the rapid development of the overland network on the mainland of Europe is part of the PLUTO story - not least because many of those who helped build it were the same men who had been involved with the installation work at the English terminals - former Pioneer Corps Sergeants Parker and Scothen, for example, who left the Isle of Wight for Normandy in the wake of D-Day:

"At last our call came - and we set foot on French soil, on the American UTAH beach. After a gruelling march inland, and a night sleeping out in the open, we split forces - three sections making their way to Nouvelle au Plain, and the remainder to Cherbourg - to start the great pipe-line which would stretch from there across the Continent to beyond the Rhine. Work was various, and every man-jack rose to the occasion. Tanks and pumping stations were erected at Querqueville (Cherbourg), Montebourg and Carentan, and a twin line, complete with valves, was laid, which necessi-

70

tated the building of bridges or tunnels in order to overcome the many obstacles in our path. Our stretch of this life-line completed (by this time the five other Pioneer Corps Companies had been assigned to various stretches along the appointed route), we 'packed our grips' and moved on to our next allocated stretch from Brionne across the River Seine to a little place called Darnetal, on the outskirts of Rouen.

"Tanks and pumping stations were erected at both Brionne (the scene of our first great fire) and Darnetal. Our old 'bogey' of camouflage once again came into the picture, and very strong winds made the job very difficult. It should be explained that these tanks and pumping stations had to be erected every 40 miles along the line to boost the petrol through it. The pumps used for this purpose were not so large as the type used at Sandown and Shanklin, but were of the same manufacture - Pearn Triple

An option for fuelling the Allied advance from France was the use of the short ship-to-shore TOMBOLA pipe-lines, which extended 100 yards offshore to enable small tankers to unload without entering harbour. (IWM)

US soldiers at an advanced railhead depot in Europe transfer petrol - delivered by the overland pipe-line network - from tanks into five-gallon cans, ready for delivery by truck to combat units. (IWM)

Ram. Whilst working on this particular stretch, we experienced many incidents which gave us cause to remember it well: a gang of boys being sniped at; the scenes of the battles in the great forest of La Londe in Normandy; finding the bodies of 20 Canadians who had been ambushed by Jerry a day after we had 'strung' that part of the line (laying out pipes along the route prior to coupling up); and taking our first prisoner - a Pole fighting in the German Army!

"With another stretch completed, our next 'jump' was a big one, for we arrived at Ostend, in Belgium. There, our task was to prepare a site and erect thereon six great tanks, the necessary pumping gear and the immediate pipe-lines. Our stay in Belgium was only a short one, for after ten weeks at Ostend we received a disappointment. Instead of 'advancing,' we were instructed to 'retreat' and, once again, found ourselves in France, at the town of Saint-Omer. At least, that was our operational HQ - we had to travel considerable distances to the actual scenes of our operations. This length of pipe extended from inside the great minefield of Calais to Wormhout, via Gravelines, Bourbourg and Esquelbeoq, with tanks at Calais and midway along at Loubourg. Like so many a Normandy stretch, it holds many memories, as we had to lay the line in rain, snow, frosts and, after the thaw, in two or three feet of squelching mud. What a life! And yet, with all the groans and moans about the 'so and so' weather, the lads worked like Trojans.

"The next move was one which delighted all of the boys, for we were informed that we were moving up into Belgium, to the small village of Sinay, 12 or so kilometres beyond Ghent. Up to this time, we had only worked alongside our own Royal Engineers, but now we joined forces with the Royal Canadian Engineers. They were fine chaps, and a grand bunch to work with. We fully enjoyed the experience.

"This stretch was similar to the others in that tanks had to be erected, pipes laid and coupled (although this time a triple line), and pumps laid into position. However, we had a new and novel task to accomplish, for this line stretched from Ghent **under** the Ghent Canal, via Dendermonde (the site for the tanks) to Antwerp, and it was the laying of the under-water pipe-line in the canal that we consider was our most ticklish problem. It was built on a wooden cradle, placed on rollers, on dry land, and resembled a capital 'A.' The joints in the line were screwed and welded, instead of being coupled. The 'launching' of this section was carried out with the aid of the US Navy and Belgian bargees, who worked the floating 75-foot cranes. A mighty task, it commenced at 2pm and finished at 4am the following day, with the Canadian film unit taking shots of the whole operation.

"This stretch completed the link-up of the whole pipe-line, reaching into the heart of Germany. We were honoured to have representatives from our Company form a guard of honour for General Sir Thomas Riddell-Webster, the Quartermaster-General, when he inserted the last four-foot length of pipe, suitably engraved with the names of all Companies who had helped to achieve this great project."

That ceremony, marking the link-up of the pipe-line from DUMBO FAR with that laid further east, took place near Termonde, north of Brussels, on 10 April 1945. "A band from the Royal Canadian Engineers celebrated the occasion with martial music," Sir Donald Banks recalled, "to the bewilderment of the Belgians, who thought the British rather crazy to succumb to such emotions about a prosaic bit of piping."

Reflecting on PLUTO

Sir Donald concluded his own entertaining account of Operation PLUTO by embracing wholeheartedly the notion that he, Mountbatten, Lloyd, Hartley, Hammick and Ellis had, indeed, been crazy - "crazy enough to dream a dream, and the dream came true." He quoted with pride - as have many others since - the overall statistics which showed that a total of 173 million gallons (some 575,000 tons) of fuel was pumped from England to France through the pipe-line under the English 'ocean' at a sustained rate - eventually - of a million gallons a day. But statistics - especially when considered in isolation - can be made to show anything.

It is necessary to probe deeper before attempting to reach a conclusion on the success, or otherwise, of Operation PLUTO. There are those who have dismissed the whole project as an abject failure or, to quote D. J. Payton-Smith, "a sad disappointment." Payton-Smith also used statistics in support of this stark assessment, pointing out that, in the crucial post-invasion period between June and October 1944, only 3,300 tons of fuel was transferred to the Continent by pipe-line. It cannot be denied that, judged against initial operational targets and objectives, the pipe-line in its original BAMBI guise did fall way below expectations. In this sense it was an undeniable failure. "PLUTO," said Payton-Smith, "contributed nothing to Allied supplies at the time when its help would have been of the greatest value - that is, when no regular oil ports were available on the Continent and the Allies were relying on the unsatisfactory Port-en-Bessin.

"DUMBO was more successful, but at a time when success was of less importance. It made no substantial contribution until the campaign in Western Europe was already more than half over; and then its average rate of throughput was little more than a tenth of total supplies across the Channel. It did not reach its peak performance (of roughly 3,300 tons a day) until after the fighting was over - and only did so after far more lines had been laid than was originally thought necessary. The fact was that the pipe-lines became unserviceable much more quickly than had been expected. Experience with the steel HAMEL pipes was particularly bad, as they developed leaks through friction with the sea bed. This technical problem does not seem to have been anticipated. By the middle of July 1945 sea bed friction had put five HAMEL pipe-lines out of action after an average life of only 56 days."

In fact, as has already been noted, the short life-expectancy of the HAMEL pipe was known from the outset, and was taken fully into account during operational preparations, while the HAIS cable gave yeoman service throughout. Neither is it fair to put all of the blame for the late start of pumping from BAMBI at the door of the PLUTO team, who could hardly be held responsible for the delay in the capture of Cherbourg.

D. J. Payton-Smith acknowledged in his study that PLUTO was much the most enterprising method for supplying oil to the Allied forces on the Continent, but added that the Chiefs of Staff never relied on it - and were wise not to do so. "In retrospect," he wrote, "it seems clear that PLUTO's advocates had been far too sanguine. They had assumed that it would be possible for the naval laying units to achieve immediately the degree of technical proficiency attained by the technically expert laying parties in the trials conducted in 1943 under the supervision of those who had

Men of 663 A. W. C. Royal Engineers were prominently involved in Operation PLUTO - on both side of the Channel. After preparation work for the BAMBI installations on the Isle of Wight, and training on PLUTO land supplies and ship-to-shore manoeuvres, the Company landed in France on D+1 and worked on the developing overland pipe-line network from the Channel ports, initially at Port-en-Bessin, then on the line from Boulogne. The Company's duties eventually took them through Belgium and Holland, then across the Rhine to the pipe-line terminal at Bocholt, in Germany. Norman Lythgoe recalls the surnames of five of the 663 A. W. C. colleagues pictured with him here: Back row: Taylor, Lythgoe, Thorpe, Hemsley. Front row: Griffin, Braithwaite and one other.
(Norman Lythgoe)

designed the equipment; and that what could be done in the Bristol Channel and the Solent could be done in wartime operational conditions on the much longer lay across the Channel." There may be some justification in that comment - but it should be borne in mind that the 70-mile run to Cherbourg was not in prospect when Operation PLUTO was 'hatched' and was considerably longer than the 20 miles or so originally envisaged. Despite that, Force PLUTO actually mastered the laying techniques very well - it was the troublesome shore-end connections which caused the most difficulty.

"Perhaps the most trenchant epitaph on PLUTO," added the Payton-Smith study, "is provided by a few figures of comparative achievement. Down to the ending of German resistance on 10 May 1945, almost 5.2 million tons of oil products were delivered to the SHAEF area through the ports of North-West Europe. Of this, about 826,000 tons came direct from across the Atlantic, and 4.3 million tons, or 84 per cent, was delivered across the Channel from England. PLUTO's contribution was only 379,000 tons, less than eight per cent of the cross-Channel supplies. This was equivalent to an average delivery rate of under 1,800 tons a day from the time when pumping began."

Again, statistics can be made to show anything. Sir Donald Banks understandably chose to quote the overall figure for delivery of fuel through the pipe-line (as, incidentally, did Clifford Hartley). D. J. Payton-Smith concentrated on the figure up until German capitulation only. Yet figures tell only part of the story. There are other ways of assessing the merits of Operation PLUTO. General Sir Thomas Riddell-Webster, for example, found one when he commented: " ... it saved a very large tanker tonnage which was badly needed in the East." This is supported in the appendices to Sir Winston Churchill's epic history of the war, where he records asking Geoffrey Lloyd in October 1944 for a short report on the progress of PLUTO. "He informs me that a cross-Channel pumping capacity of 1,000,000 gallons of petrol a day is aimed at. A figure of this magnitude must effect a large saving of tankers and manpower ..." That figure was, as noted earlier, eventually attained.

Above all, PLUTO was a remarkable conception which, throughout its rapid voyage of wartime development in often uncharted waters, demanded the highest levels of ingenuity, technical expertise, commitment, energy and co-operation from all those who took part in it. They were not found wanting in any of these respects.

"It was second in daring only to the artificial harbours project," said General Eisenhower, the Supreme Allied Commander. "It was a great scheme, a great effort, a great achievement, and a great success," say former Sergeants Parker and Scothen. "It can go down in history as one of the secret weapons that helped to bring about the defeat of Germany."

Overleaf:
An official souvenir pamphlet issued by 21 Army Group to mark the completion near Termonde, Belgium, of the connection between the pipe-line from PLUTO at Boulogne and that laid further east - the final link in the pipe-line chain between England and Germany - on 19 April 1945. The pamphlet was signed by Captain Maurice Lickens, who commanded 44 Platoon E & M, Royal Engineers. Preserved in the Imperial War Museum archives, it was rediscovered there by Mr. Lickens half-a-century later! It is almost certainly the only one remaining in existence. (IWM)

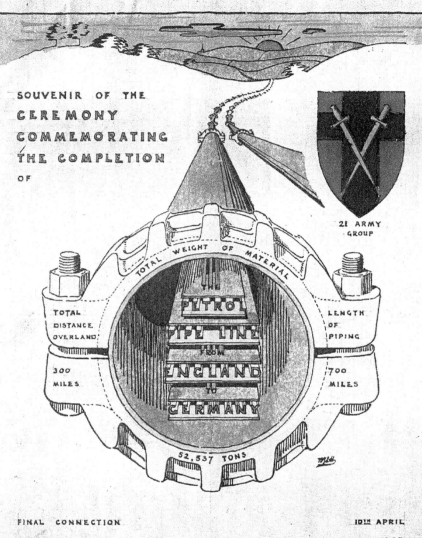

SOUVENIR OF THE
CEREMONY
COMMEMORATING
THE COMPLETION
OF

21 ARMY GROUP

TOTAL WEIGHT OF MATERIAL

TOTAL DISTANCE OVERLAND

LENGTH OF PIPING

THE PETROL PIPE LINE FROM ENGLAND TO GERMANY

300 MILES

700 MILES

52,537 TONS

FINAL CONNECTION
MADE BY

10TH APRIL
1945

GENERAL SIR THOMAS S. RIDDELL-WEBSTER KCB, DSO
Q.M.G. TO THE FORCES

Chapter 11
1945-95: PIPE-LINE POST-SCRIPT

The recovery

The pipe-lines which were PLUTO slumbered on the sea bed for little more than a year. No longer a highly-regarded secret weapon of war, they became a thorough nuisance. The HAIS cable in particular repeatedly fouled anchorages, and its magnetic field created havoc with the GPO's attempts to accurately locate breaks in their own cross-Channel cables. But the pipe-line cables *were* in demand. The post-war shortage of lead saw to that. It was fetching up to £55 a ton - a goodly sum in the late 1940s - and there was 65 tons of lead in every nautical mile of HAIS. So, in the autumn of 1946, a major salvage operation began to recover the redundant cable and, with it, the 23,000 tons of lead making up its inner core. The salvage contract was let by the Ministry of Supply to a private firm, Marine Contractors Ltd., whose first job was to find out where the cable lines lay. In order to clear inshore anchorages, the Royal Navy had recovered the shore-end sections, and cut lengths of the main cable three miles out. The severed ends had been dropped back in the water and, in most cases, had sunk into the sand or mud.

"Dragging grapples, ships steamed about the area charted by the Navy and hooked the pipes about four miles out," reported *Soldier*, the British Army's magazine, in October 1946. "These were cut, plugged with wood, and the ends were marked with red and yellow buoys; the mile section inland of the cut was collected, and ships prepared for the main task." That, of course, was to recover the cable in mid-Channel. For this job, the contractors had the perfect ship lined up. She was just under 7,000 tons, a Liberty ship built in 1941 for the Ministry of War Transport and named the *Empire Ridley*. During the latter part of the war she had operated under a different name and been specially converted for *laying* cable.

Force "PLUTO"

1942 – 1945

"H.M.S. LATIMER"

Dear *Reeves*

Our very pleasant association in Force "PLUTO" is now coming to an end. I think we may look back at our work together of the last two years, and espeially recently since D Day, with a feeling of some pride and satisfacton.

We have done our job a·d made it work, and in so doing have contributed not a little to the final victory as is our duty. Our work has been unique in Hitory.

I feel that we have been very·much a "Band of Brothers" and I hope that though now sparating officially this precious tie may not be broken and that "PLUTOS" will always hail each other with joyous remembrance.

I want to express to you personally my very great thanks for your loyal and energetic support throughout the operation.

Yours very sincerely

J-F. Lut Olwwy

Cap·ain Royal Navy,
Senior Naval Officer Commanding Force "PLUTO."

Along with other members of HMS Latimer's crew, Jim Reeves received this letter of thanks from Force PLUTO's SNO, Captain Hutchings, in 1945. Though somewhat 'battle-scarred,' it remains a treasured memento of unusual wartime service. (Jim Reeves)

Two years after making that first historic run to Shanklin Pier from Nacqueville in August 1944, the former HMS *Latimer* set about the task of retrieving the cable she had laid.

An old minesweeper turned tug-tender picked up the first buoy, attached it to the end of the pipe-line and linked it to the *Empire Ridley* with a rocket-boom line. "The rope attached to the pipe-line was wound round the great winch and along the carrier and booster wheels on deck, from the bows to the after-hold," added *Soldier*. "Then the end of PLUTO came out of the sea and up through the bows. Foot by foot, it was coaxed round the winch and along the decks by a gang of men with iron bars. Four hours after the rocket line landed on the *Empire Ridley's* forecastle, the first coil of PLUTO was being laid round the circumference of the hold."

Progressing across the Channel, the salvage team recovered the cable at a rate of six miles a day, under the watchful eye of Clifford Hartley, for whom this must have been a bitter-sweet occasion, and Brigadier G. A. Sims, from the War Office, whose task was to examine the HAIS cable to see how it had coped with more than two years on the sea bed. He found it to be in excellent condition, with almost no marine growth or barnacles, and no rusting to the outer steel tape covering the lead, which had been exposed during recovery. The *Empire Ridley* did not enjoy a trouble-free crossing. Two-and-a-half days after picking up the cable, with more than twelve miles of it stowed on board, she lost it again when it snapped while the ship was riding out a gale 16 miles off the Isle of Wight. However, in the end, there was no doubting the success of **this** operation. The *Empire Ridley* was later joined by sister ships and, of that 23,000 tons of lead in the HAIS cable, all but 1,000 tons was recovered. Hartley must have taken particular satisfaction from the discovery within the cable of substantial quantities of petrol - a total of 75,000 gallons was recovered by the close of the operation.

There was just as much demand for steel in post-war Britain, and 3,300 tons of the 5,500 tons of steel in the abandoned HAMEL pipes was also recovered during the salvage exercise, which continued for the best part of three years, finally ending in July 1949.

When Operation PLUTO was featured by the *Daily Mail* in September 1994, several readers wrote to the newspaper with information on the subsequent use of pipe-line parts. Sections of HAIS cable were cut up in lengths of between 20 and 30 feet in the post-war years, and stored at Southampton, a Swansea reader revealed. From there, they were taken to a Ministry of Defence foundry at Swansea, where the pipe was stripped of its outer armouring until only the lead inner remained. It was then transported back to Southampton to be melted down. A reader from Hertfordshire, meanwhile, recalled working after the war at a tube mill near Desford, Leicestershire, where pieces of PLUTO were apparently sent in 1950 to be made into railway engine boiler tubes designed for export to Argentina.

The relics

Beneath the sea, some short sections of pipe-line missed during the salvage have come to light - particularly off the Isle of Wight, following a sonar and diving survey there. With colleagues, Martin Woodward, who runs Bembridge Maritime Museum on the Island, recovered a few pieces of HAIS cable, some of which are now displayed in his own, and other, museums.

More recently, Mr. Woodward has located - again by sonar - what appears to be a length of HAMEL pipe.

Among the other surviving artefacts are two of the massive PLUTO pumps. One is on display at the Imperial War Museum; the other is stored by the IWM at Duxford

Sixty-five yards of the pipe-line which once gravity-fed the BAMBI terminal at Shanklin, Isle Wight, remain in place to this day - carefully restored and maintained - as a unique tourist attraction for visitors to the historic gorge of Shanklin Chine. (Brian Bradbury / Shanklin Chine)

Airfield, Cambridgeshire, with plans quite literally in the pipe-line to have it moved to the Isle of Wight for permanent exhibition there. At Hamble oil refinery in Hampshire, a rusty pipe-line valve from PLUTO was thoroughly cleaned in 1994 and reinstated, complete with visitors' information board, on the 50th anniversary of its original installation. In Germany, parts of the old military pipe-line which connected with PLUTO have been maintained and upgraded for modern-day use.

But, without a doubt, the most evocative reminders of Pipe-Line Under the Ocean itself remain intact, and unmoved in contrasting situations on the Isle of Wight - as the pictures opposite and overleaf show.

Exposed at low tide, 12 shore-end pipe connections at the Thorness Bay SOLO pipe-line terminal on the Isle of Wight have survived half-a-century of battering by the sea. They were pictured in April 1995. (Matt Searle)

Appendix I

Pluto acronyms and code-names

PLUTO	Pipe-Line Under The Ocean
	Pipe-Line Underwater Transport of Oil
SOLO	Pipe-line under the Solent
TOTO	Reservoir, Hungerberry Copse, Shanklin
TOMBOLA	Ship-to-shore pipe-lines
TWEEDLEDUM	Bournemouth Bay laying trials
HAIS	Hartley-Anglo Iranian-Siemens cable
HAMEL	Hammick-Ellis steel pipe
HAIS-HAMEL	Combination of above (one end)
HAIS-HAMEL-HAIS	ditto (both ends)
BAMBI	Sandown-Shanklin pumping stations
WATSON	Nacqueville (Cherbourg) pumping station
DUMBO	Dungeness pumping station
DUMBO FAR	Boulogne pumping station
CONUNDRUM	Steel (cone-ended) drum
CONUM	Short form for above

Appendix 2

Companies contributing to Operation PLUTO

From *Operation Pluto*, by A. C. Hartley, C.B.E., B.Sc., M.I.C.E.,
Institution of Civil Engineers - *Civil Engineer at War* papers, Vol 3

HAIS cable
(1) In the development and manufacture of the first experimental length.
  Anglo-Iranian Oil Co. Ltd.
  Siemens Brothers & Co. Ltd.

(2) In the production of the first 30-mile lengths and full-scale tests.
  Those listed in (1), and
  W. T. Henley's Telegraph Works Co. Ltd.
  Johnson and Phillips Ltd.
  National Oil Refineries Ltd.

(3) In the manufacture, testing and laying of the operational lenhgths.
  Those listed in (1) & (2), and
  Callender's Cable and Construction Co. Ltd.
  Pirelli General Cable Works.
  W. T. Glover & Co. Ltd.
  Standard Telephones and Cables Ltd.
  Edison Swan Electric Co. Ltd.
  Telegraph Construction and Maintenance Co.

HAMEL pipe

Stewarts and Lloyds Ltd.
Anglo-Iranian Oil Co. Ltd.
Iraq Petroleum Co. Ltd.
A. I. Welding Machines Ltd.
British Insulated Cables Ltd.
Oil Well Engineering Co.
Orthostyle Ltd.
John Mowlem & Co. Ltd.
Renold and Coventry Chain Co. Ltd.
J. & E. Hall.
British Thomson Houston Co. Ltd.

Construction of pumping terminals and supply of pumping plant etc.

Anglo-Iranian Oil Co. Ltd.
National Oil Refineries Ltd.
Kinnear Moodie & Co. Ltd.
Frank Pearn & Co. Ltd.
Jack Olding & Co. Ltd.
Mather and Platt Ltd.
Victaulic Co. Ltd.
A. Reyrolle & Co. Ltd.
Isle of Wight Electric Light and Power Co.
Folkestone Electricity Supply Co. Ltd.
County of London Electric Supply Co. Ltd.

Appendix 3

The 3-inch HAIS cable

From *Operation Pluto*, by A. C. Hartley, C.B.E., B.Sc., M.I.C.E.
Institution of Civil Engineers - *Civil Engineer at War* papers, Vol 3.

The lead sheath for HAIS Cable is manufactured in continuous lengths of 700 yards and wound on wooden drums having a barrel diameter of not less than 79 inches. The sheath has an internal bore of 3.05 inches and a minimum lead thickness of 0.175 inch, and, subject to usual manufacturers' tolerances, the outer diameter of the sheath is approximately 3.446 inches.

The drums are then placed behind the armouring machine and each individual length is joined by lead burning to the continuous length being armoured. An internal pressure of 25 lb. per square inch is applied during armouring.

The materials used in order of application on the lead sheath are as follows:

(a)   Petroleum residue compound.
(b)   Two layers of compound paper tape, approximately 2.5 inches wide, 0.010 inch thick, applied left-hand lay, giving a gap of approximately 0.1 inch.
(c)   One lay of compound cotton tape, approximately 3 inches wide, having an overlap of one-eighth inch.
(d)   Four layers of steel tape, 2 inches wide, 0.022 inch thick, applied right-hand lay, breaking joint approximately 60/40 with a gap of

0.15 inch. Individual tapes are joined by cutting at about 30 degrees to the length of the tape and lap spot welded. Approximate diameter over steel tapes: 3.72 inches.

(e) Petroleum residue compound over steel tapes.

(f) First serving of single-ply jute bedding. Right-hand lay.

(g) Petroleum residue compound over the jute applied at armouring die.

(h) 57 by 0.192 inch diameter galvanised mild-steel wire, applied left-hand lay at about 30 inch lay. Approximate diameter over armouring wires: 4.19 inches. Individual lengths of armouring wire are joined by butt fusion.

(i) Petroleum residue compound over armouring wires.

(j) Second serving of single-ply jute, right-hand lay.

(k) Petroleum residue compound over jute.

(l) Third serving of three-ply jute, applied left-hand.

(m) Petroleum residue compound over jute.

(n) Coating over compound of whitewash solution.

Note: Final specifications given by other sources differ slightly in minor detail - e.g. the compound paper tape is described as 2 inches wide, rather than 2.5, and the compound copper tape, as 2.25 inches, rather than 3.

Specification of materials

Lead (alloy E): 0.15 to 0.25 per cent antimony.
0.35 to 0.45 per cent tin.

Steel tapes: Ultimate strength - 25 tons per square inch.
Minimum yield - 20 tons per square inch.
Elongation of 10-inch length - 10 per cent.

Armouring wires: Tensile strength - 25 to 30 tons per square inch.
Elongation of 10-inch length - 12 per cent min.

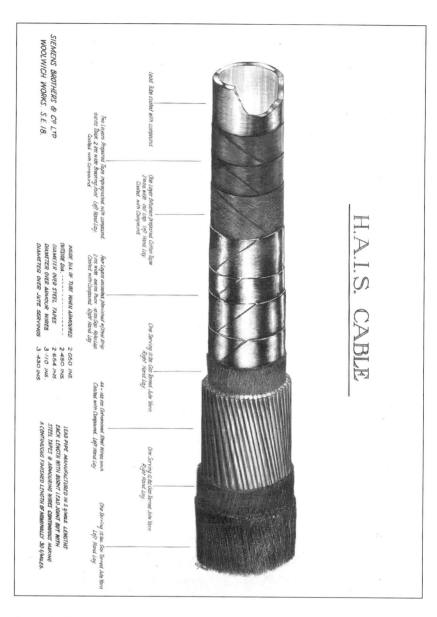

H.A.I.S. CABLE

Lead Tube coated with compound

Two Layers Prepared Tape impregnated with compound. 9/1000 Thick 2 ins wide Bearing Joint. Left Hand Lay. Coated with Compound.

One Layer Bitumen Prepared Cotton Tape. 2 ins wide. 1/8" Gap. Left Hand Lay. Coated with Compound.

Four Layers uncoated, Varnished w/Silver Ship. 2 ins wide. 1/2 ins Thick, 1/16 Gap. 9/64 Gap. Coated with Compound. Right Hand Lay.

One Serving 12 lbs Coir Tarred Jute Yarn. Right Hand Lay.

44 x 182 ins Galvanised Steel Wires each. Coated with Compound. Left Hand Lay.

One Serving 12 lbs Coir Tarred Jute Yarn. Right Hand Lay.

One Serving 13 lbs Coir Tarred Jute Yarn. Left Hand Lay.

INSIDE DIA. OF TUBE WHEN ARMOURED	2·050 INS.
OUTSIDE DIA.	2·450 INS.
DIAMETER OVER STEEL TAPES	2·654 INS.
DIAMETER OVER ARMOUR WIRES	3·110 INS.
DIAMETER OVER JUTE SERVINGS	3·430 INS.

LEAD PIPE MANUFACTURED IN 5 1/2 MILE LENGTHS
EACH LENGTH WITH BURNT LEAD JOINT BUT WITH
STEEL TAPES & ARMOURING WIRES CONTINUOUS MAKING
A CONTINUOUS FINISHED LENGTH OF NOMINALLY 30 1/2 MILES.

SIEMENS BROTHERS & C° LTD
WOOLWICH WORKS. S.E.18.

Siemens' official manufacturers' picture-diagram of the three-inch HAIS cable.
(Charles Brown)

90

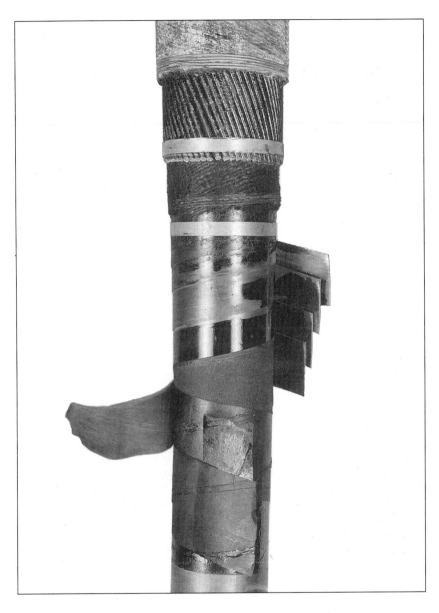

A partially-exploded view of the three-inch HAIS cable showing the lead pipe, armour protection and protective servings of jute. (Charles Brown)

Above: *Terminal end of HAIS cable. (Charles Brown)*
Below: *The cable in cross-section. (Charles Brown)*

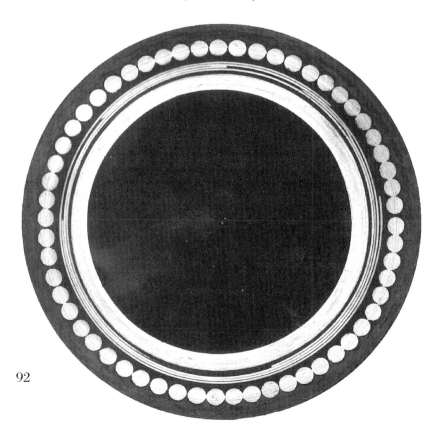

THE HAIS. CABLE COUPLING

Labels (top, left to right): OUTER JUTE SERVINGS · ARMOUR WIRES · INNER JUTE SERVING · STEEL TAPES · LEAD PIPE

Labels (A section): 5226/1-101. · 5226/2-102. · 5226/5-105. · 5226/6 -106 · 5226/5A-105A. · 5226/3-103 · 5226/9-109 · 5226/8-108 · 5226/4 -104. · 'U' JOINT RINGS TYPES. 191-192. · 5226/7-107 · 'HAT' JOINT TYPE. E. · 5226/14 -104. · FLANGED LEAD PIPE

Label (B section): 5226/10-10 -110 · 5226/12

(A) SHEWS METHOD OF COUPLING TWO CABLE ENDS BY MEANS OF THE SPLIT MUFF

(B) SHEWS COUPLING END WITH SWIVEL YOKE END ATTACHED FOR HAULING.

NOTE · TERMINAL END, 5226/11.-III. IS FITTED IN PLACE OF 2 IN SIMILAR MANNER TO 5226/10.-110. WHERE REQUIRED.

NOTE · PART NUMBERS· 5226/1.TO II. REFER TO 3 INCH COUPLINGS – 5226/101.TOIII. REFER TO 2 INCH COUPLINGS.
UNIT- PART Nº 5226/12. IS INTERCHANGEABLE FOR BOTH SIZES OF COUPLINGS.

— SIEMENS BROTHERS & CO. LTD. —

Manufacturers' picture-diagram of the HAIS cable coupling. (Charles Brown)

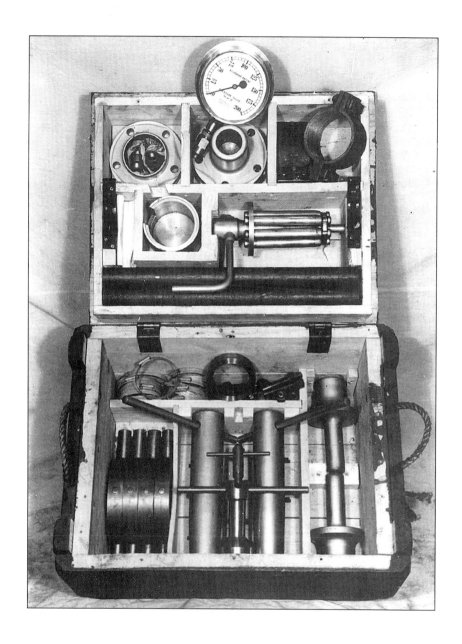

Special toolbox for HAIS cable coupling spare parts. (Charles Brown)

Appendix 4

HAIS cable bursting discs

Method of operation as described by A. C. Hartley ...

The bursting discs were fitted to the HAIS cable joints to contain water under pressure in the cables until laid and connected. When a line was ready for commissioning, a pump was started and the rate of rise of pressure was recorded. At first the rise was slow, and when 400 lb/sq was reached the first disc was broken and the pressure was seen to fall immediately - and then begin slowly to rise again. This was repeated at each disc until the arrival of liquid was reported at the further end by direct telephone.

... and by Sir Donald Banks

The thrill of making the first tests (with the HAIS cable) were notable. The cable was filled with water when being laid in order to give necessary strengthening to the hollow core, to enable it to withstand the strains of passing over the laying machinery and the pressure of the sea when it reached the bottom. At intervals in the cross-Channel length, thin metal discs were inserted to contain the water, and these were devised to burst at pressures of 400 lb/sq. When the lay was reported complete, the pumps were coupled-up and more water pumped in from the home end. Anxious faces would gather round the pressure meter in the control room to watch the needle climb steadily to the bursting pressure of the first disc, and a sigh of relief would go up when it suddenly wobbled and fell back again. The first disc had blown satisfactorily.

Successively, one disc after another would be negotiated, the excitement growing as the last ones were reached. Eventually, some one-and-three-quarter hours after the commencement of pumping, the final one would go and a welcome telephone call from the other side would announce 'line on flow.' Water was gushing out on the beach at Boulogne. Oil would then be substituted for water, and it normally took about 24 hours before the first traces appeared across on the other side, when a halt was called while the pipe was connected to the tankage system. The residual water was strained off by the simple expedient of letting it settle to the bottom of the tanks, and draining it from there, the oil floating naturally to the top. As soon as the oil flow in the pipes became pure enough for direct use, the line was pronounced operational.

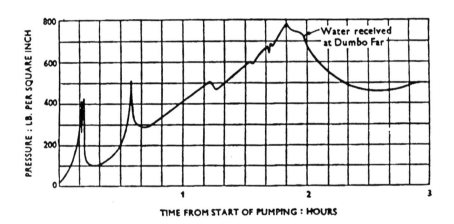

Graph of a water test on a cross-Channel three-inch HAIS cable line running from the DUMBO terminal in Dungeness. (MoD - Naval Historical Branch)

Appendix 5

Force PLUTO: The fleet

Cable ships
Algerian (2,315 tons; built 1924 / formerly Ellerman merchant vessel)
Holdfast (1,499 tons; built 1921 / formerly Dundee, Perth & London
    cargo ship *London*)
Latimer (6,987 tons; built 1941 / formerly Min. of War Transport
    vessel *Empire Ridley*)
Sancroft (6,978 tons; built 1941 / formerly Min. of War Transport
    vessel *Empire Baffin*)

Hopper barge
Persephone
(HM hopper barge W.24)

Trawlers
Cedar
Grampian

Cable barges
Britannic
Goldbell
Golddrift
Oceanic
Runic

Accomodation barges
Aeton
Glenmoriston
Lawson
Nyctea

Steel drums
Conundrums
(Conums) I to VI

Towing tugs
Bustler
Danube V
Marauder

Appendix 6

PLUTO - June 1944: Definition of Responsibilities between Government and Service Departments

From *The Second World War: Army (Supplies and Transport - Volume II)*. The War Office, 1954.

1. Petroleum Warfare Department

Responsible for:

(a) Provision of materials, except petroleum products; technical design, development and provision of materials, including spare parts, for technical plant and machinery, in collaboration with Service Departments concerned.

(b) Financial relations with Treasury for matters concerned with the above provision,

(c) Experiments, technical advice and co-ordination of progress.

(d) Operation and technical supervision of the United Kingdom terminals, and repairs to plant there.

(e) Connecting up sea lines above high water mark on United Kingdom shore.

(f) Provision of specialised couplings for the far shore, for use by British or US military engineers concerned.

2. Directorate of Supplies and Transport

Responsible for:

(a) Provision of RASC personnel to operate the United Kingdom terminals, and carry out minor repairs.

(b) Provision of, and accounting for, the petroleum products (in conjunction with Air Ministry for aviation fuels) as required by SHAEF to the maximum capacity of the plant.

(c) Notifying the Petroleum Board and the Petroleum Warfare Department when pumping operations were to begin, and when the feeder systems were to be charged; also, from time to time, the quantities and grades of petroleum products required to be delivered through PLUTO in accordance with demands.

3. Allied Naval Commander, Expeditionary Force (ANCXF)

Responsible for:

(a) General control of the actual operation of establishing PLUTO. (The laying of the pipe-lines was carried out by Senior Naval Officer, PLUTO).

(b) Ordering the beginning of the operation after consultation with the Commander of the Armies in the Field, and notifying all concerned of the issue of orders to begin laying.

(c) Maintenance and repair of all sea cable and pipe-lines.

4. Ministry of Fuel and Power - Petroleum Division

Responsible for:

General departmental supervision of petroleum supply arrangements in the United Kingdom (except terminal pump stations), in conjunction with the War Office, Petroleum Warfare Department and the Petroleum Board.

5. Army in the Field

During the period when C-in-C, 21 Army Group, was responsible for the administration of all ground forces on the Continent, HQ, 21 Army Group, was responsible, irrespective of whether the far shore terminals were manned by British or US personnel, for:

(a) Notifying SHAEF, ANCXF and War Office when pipe-lines could be accepted into the theatre of operations.

(b) Hauling ashore the cable and pipe-lines when presented for acceptance by ANCXF, and coupling up to storage.

(c) Provision of necessary terminal facilities for the reception of petroleum products to be delivered by PLUTO.

(d) Arrangements for the provision of the necessary communications between terminals.

(e) Notifying War Office of readiness on far shore for pumping operations to begin.

(f) Notifying War Office (ST 2) of the quantities and grades of petroleum products required to be delivered by means of PLUTO.

When the Supreme Commander allocated a separate area of responsibility to First (US) Army Group:

(a) SHAEF assumed responsibility for deciding the policy for the further development of the PLUTO project, and for issuing executive instructions to ANCXF, and British and US Army Groups.

(b) Supreme Commander also became responsible for notifying War Office (ST 2) of grades and quantities of petroleum products required to be delivered by means of PLUTO.

Appendix 7

PLUTO - April 1945: Division of Responsibilities between RE and RASC for supply of POL by pipe-line

From *The Second World War: Army (Supplies and Transport - Volume II)*. The War Office, 1954.

1. The Royal Engineers

Responsible for:

(a) The design, in co-operation with the RASC, of all installations and pipe-lines for the storage and movement of POL.

(b) Calculation for provision purposes of all stores required for the erection of bulk storage installations, pump stations and pipe-lines.

(c) Provision, storage and shipment of all stores required for the construction of installations and work, referred to in (a) above.

(d) The erection of tankage, laying of pipe-lines, and installation of plant, including testing the installations and lines before handing over to the RASC.

(e) Maintenance work beyond the capacity of the RASC operating personnel, and tools.

2. The Royal Army Service Corps

Responsible for:

(a) The detailed planning and provision of the requirements of POL within staff policy, research, design of equipment (other than that specified in 1 (a) above), formulation of requirements of RE supply, maintenance of statistics, operation of installations, storage, issue and accountancy.

(b) The staffing and operation of all storage installations, including pumping stations on main and subsidiary pipe-line routes.

(c) The maintenance, patrolling and inspection of pipe-lines between installations and pump stations.

(d) Arrangements with the Royal Corps of Signals for the provision of signal communications throughout the length of pipe-line routes.

(e) The normal day-to-day maintenance involved in the execution of the above tasks.

(f) Advising the RE wherever technical oil questions arose regarding the storage of POL in bulk and movements by pipe-line.

(g) Action with the Army Fire Services in regard to the provision of the necessary fire-fighting services. (Engineer works services was responsible for any works services involved.)

Appendix 8

High-pressure petrol pipe-lines
North-West Europe: 1944-45

Statistics for pipe-lines constructed, operated and maintained by British Liberation Army (21 Army Group) - from records held at the Imperial War Museum and research by Maurice Lickens, a former Royal Engineers officer , who helped to compile the statistics in 1945 .

Routes from PLUTO based on diagrammatic layout compiled in September 1945 by 548 & 796 E & M Companies, Royal Engineers, showing mileage between pumping stations:

1. From BAMBI route - Cherbourg (Querqueville) to Montebourg (single line), 21. Montebourg to Isigny (single line), 20. Isigny to Port-en-Bessin (single line), 18.5. Port-en-Bessin to Bronay (double line), 15.5. Bronay to Billy (double line), 21. Billy to Glos (double line), 24. Glos to Brionne (double line), 23. Brionne to Rouen (double line), 20. Rouen to Darnetal (double line), 13. Darnetal to Fourgette (double line), 2. Total pipe-line mileage: shown: 178. Total piping mileage (including lengths in installations): 367.5.

Spur pipe-lines (all single line) - (a) Port-en-Bessin to Juvigny, 7. (b) Port-en-Bessin to Coulombs, 14. Coulombs to Carpiquet, 8. (c) Bronay to Ouistreham, 16.

System ceased operation - January 1945. The shut-down was supervised by former Captain Lickens, commanding 548 Platoon, Electrical & Mechanical Company, Royal Engineers.

Note - The long pipe-line from the Cotentin to Frankfurt, Germany, via

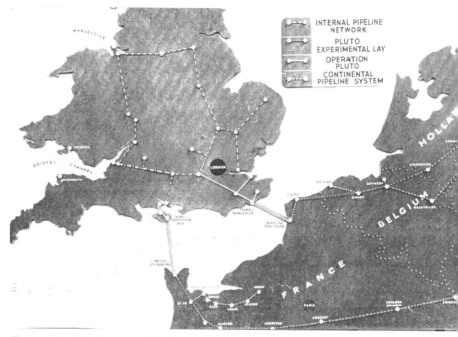

INTERNAL PIPELINE
NETWORK
PLUTO
EXPERIMENTAL LAY
OPERATION
PLUTO
CONTINENTAL
PIPELINE SYSTEM

The completel pipe-line network, showing all lines constructed by British and American forces. (IWM)

Chartres and Chalons, is not included above as this was constructed and maintained by the Americans.

2. From DUMBO route - Boulogne to Calais (triple line), 19.9. Calais to Loobergne, Belgium (double line), 21.4. Loobergne to Eikhoek (double line), 20.2. Eikhoek to Coucheleere (double line), 16. Coucheleere to Beernem (double line), 21.3. Beernem to Ghent (double line), 21. Ghent to Termonde (double line), 21. Termonde to Contich (double line), 20. Contich to Herentals (double line), 17.5. Herentals to Lommel (double line), 23.1. Lommel to Eindhoven, Holland (double line), 20. Eindhoven to St. Antnonis (double line), 19. St. Antnonis to Reichswald, Germany (double line), 19. Reichswald to Emmerich (double line), 10.3. Emmerich to Bocholt (single line),   19. Total pipe-line mileage shown: 288.7. Total piping mileage (including lengths in installations): 700.

Spur pipes-lines (both double line) - (a) Beernem to Ostend, 19.4. (b) Contich to Antwerp, 6.5. Antwerp to Hemixem, 4.

Main system ceased operation - 12 August 1945 (from Ghent - 28 August; from Contich - 2 September).

Note (a) - The pipe-line from Antwerp to Wesel, Germany, via Maastricht, is not included above as this was constructed and maintained by the Americans.

Note (b) - The total mileage indicated is the accumulation of distances shown on the diagrammatic layout. However, unlike the Cherbourg route - where the individual and overall figures tally - the same document refers to a total mileage of 340 miles.

Note (c) - There were also some highly unofficial additions to the system. Maurice Lickens recalls the tapping of the pipe-line by local people near Herentals, Belgium, and the running of a branch main to outbuildings nearby! "Petrol was a very valuable commodity - at that time it really was liquid gold we were dealing with."

Total number of gallons pumped by both British systems - 350 million (250 million of which was transported along the main line from Boulogne to Bocholt). Pumping was continuous - 24 hours a day, seven days a week. 21 Army Group calculated in July 1945 that the amount of petrol which had by then been pumped was equivalent to the transportation of one ton of petrol over a distance of 100 million miles - further than the distance between the Earth and the Sun!

Losses - The worst monthly loss of fuel - through damage, spillage or theft - from the pipe-line system was 1.8 per cent. Overall, the loss figure was considerably less than 1 per cent.

Main piping used - Six-inch Victaulic.

Total weight of materials used (by April 1945) - 52,537 tons.

Army units involved in construction work - Royal Engineers: SCRE Works, 106 & 107. Works Sections RE, 210, 212. HQ E & M Companies, 545, 547, 548, 796. Type A Platoons, E & M, 38, 46. Type B Platoons, E & M, 39, 40, 43, 44, 47, 48, 61, 62, 63, 64, 65, 66, 70. Mechanical

Equipment Platoons, 16. Welding Platoons, 1. Stores Sections, 17, 22. Art. Works Companies, 662, 663, 666, 677. Royal Army Service Corps: GT Companies, 378, 710, 714, 718. Pioneer Corps Companies, 13, 36, 70, 308, 328, 282. Royal Canadian Engineers, 3 Battalion, 2 Drilling Company.

Maurice Lickens - who now lives on Isle of Wight, a location so closely associated with Operation PLUTO - summed up the Contintental operation as follows: "It was a fantastic concept, and in many ways it was a miracle it worked as well as it did - because we had chaps like me who really knew nothing about pipe-lines before we started.

"It was a quick learning process and, in order to achieve what was required of us, we all had to work like beavers in far from easy conditions. It was hard graft throughout, with none of the comforts usually laid on for military units ... no canteens, no entertainment, nothing like that at all. I think it is fair to say an incredibly good job was done in a remarkably short space of time. Certainly, we were all very proud of it."

Bibliography

Principal sources

Banks, Sir Donald. *Flame over Britain* (Sampson, Low, Marston & Co., London), 1946.

Beavis, E. A. *Development of the HAIS Cable - in Engineering Bulletin* 224 (Siemens Bros. & Co., London), 1946.

Boileau, Colonel D. W. *Supplies and Transport*, Vols. I & II - in *The Second World War 1939-45: Army* (The War Office, London), 1954.

Hartley, A. C. *Operation PLUTO* - reprint of paper (Royal Society of Arts, London), 1945.

Chandler, David / Lawton-Collins, James Jr. *The D-Day Encyclopedia.* (Simon and Schuster, New York, USA), 1994.

Ellis, L. F. *Victory in the West, Vol. II* (Imperial War Museum, London/Battery Press, Nasville USA), 1994.

Hartley, A. C. (edit). *Instructions for fitting modified HAIS Cable Couplings* (Petroleum Warfare Dept. / Siemens Bros. & Co., London), 1945.

Hartley, A. C. Operation PLUTO - in *The Engineer at War - A symposium of papers on war-time engineering problems* (Institution of Civil Engineers, London), 1948.

Hyland, Paul. *Wight: Biography of an Island* (Victor Gollancz, London), 1984.

Lascelles, Richard. *Pulling up PLUTO* - in *Soldier* magazine, Vol. 2, No. 13 (British Army), October 1946.

Kemp, Norman. *The Devices of War* (Werner Laurie, London), 1956,

Payton-Smith, D. J. *Oil - A study of war-time policy and administration* (HMSO, London), 1971.

Reekie, Doug;las. *These Were the Nerves - The story of the electric cable and wire industry of Great Britain during the years of war* (Insulated Conductors Export Group, London), 1946.

Searle, Adrian. *The Isle of Wight at War - 1939-45* (Dovecote Press, Dorset), 1989.

Tute, Warren / Costello, John / Hughes, Terry. *D-Day* (Sidgwick & Jackson, London), 1974.

Uncredited. *The End of PLUTO* - in Royal Army Service Corps journal, Vol. 71, No. 9 (RASC), June 1947.

Original documents

Public Record Office. Directorate of Supplies and Transport papers WO 272 (9 to 23), 1942-45.

Periodicals

Various articles in: *British Trade Journal & Export World. Daily Mail. Daily Mirror, Electrical Industries. Electrical Review. The Electrician. Engineering. The Engineer. The Islander. Petroleuum Times. Shipping World. The Times.*

Acknowledgements

This book would not have been possible without Anne Springman, the owner of Shanklin Chine, who, with the help of a hard-working committee, has masterminded two superb exhibitions there in 1994 and 1995 to mark the 50th anniversaries of, respectively, the Normandy landings and the victorious conclusion of the war. Indeed, the book was born out of the immense interest shown by visitors - particularly veterans of the operation - in the PLUTO memorabilia on display at the Chine, together with the surviving section of pipe-line which runs through it.

So much marvellous information was forwarded to Anne that she was led to conclude that a book chronicling for the first time the whole fascinating story of PLUTO was long overdue. I am grateful to her for entrusting me with the task of writing it - grateful, too, for her unbounded enthusiasm for the project, and the practical help she has provided in getting it 'off the ground.' My thanks also go to Michael, Anne's husband, for his invaluable input.

Grateful appreciation is due to Messrs. Crossprint, for the excellent design and production of the book in a relatively short space of time - and for their patient understanding (I hope!) of the processes involved in rounding-up the material in the first place.

We are greatly indebted to Lord Prior, Chairman of GEC, for contributing the foreword, and also for providing valuable additional information relating to the engineering aspects of the story. Our thanks go, too, to Lord Mottistone, Governor of the Isle of Wight, for his help in seeking Lord Prior's involvement.

Many other people have helped to provide what we hope is a well-rounded account of the PLUTO story. In particular, the following deserve our thanks for their contributions to the project: Sarah Brotherton-Ratcliffe, Charles Brown, Ronald Crabtree, Reg Langstaffe, Maurice Lickens, Museum of Army Transport, Norman Lythgoe, Reg Parker, Lt. Colonel C. E. Penn , Jim Reeves, Raymond Salter, Ben Scothen, Major J. A. Starling (23 Pioneer Regt., Royal Logistic Corps) and Martin Woodward.

Index

Beernem, Belgium - 104.

Belgium & Belgians - 67, 72, 73, 75 (see also specific locations).

Belle Mead USASF depot, New Jersey - 55.

Bembridge Maritime Museum, Isle of Wight - 82.

Billy, France - 103.

Bochalt, Germany - 75, 104.

Boulogne - DUMBO FAR terminal & pumping station - 9, 58, 63, 66, 67, 69; code-name, 64; port & harbour, 63; seafront, 67; HAIS-HAMEL at, 66,67; Hotel Imperial, 67; Fort de la Creche, 67; connections with Continental network, 69, 73, 75, 77, 78, 104; Ambleteuse beach, 63.

Bourbourg, France - 72.

Bournemouth Bay - 52.

Brionne, France - 71, 103.

Bristol Channel - tanker ports, 15, 40; pipe-line trials, 22, 27-30, 37, 59, 76.

British Expeditionary Force (BEF) - 67.

British Insulated Cables Ltd. - 87.

British Liberation Forces & 21 Army Group - 56. 57, 69, 77, 78, 99, 100, 103, 105.

British Thomson Houston Co. Ltd. - 87.

Bronay, France - 103.

Brussels - 73.

Burmah Oil Co. - 32.

Bustler, HMS - 52.

Cable barges - 97.

Cable ships - 33, 40, 41, 51, 59, 60, 67, 97 (see also specific ships).

Caen, France - 57.

Calais, France - 41, 69, 72, 104.

Callender's Cable & Construction Co. - 31, 86.

Camouflage, concealment & subterfuge - pipe-line, 45, 49, 50, 71; terminals & pumps, 45, 46, 48; reservoir, 44.

Canadian forces - 72, 73 (see also specific units).

21, 22, 30; manufacture of cable, 22-25, 30, 53, 54, 86; & of lead piping, 23; loading, carrying & laying, 24, 40, 41, 57, 63, 64, 86; shore ends & connections, 27, 28, 52, 59, 63, 64, 76; three-inch development, 30, 39, 88-92; cross-Solent pipe-line, 44; first cross Channel lay, 58, 59; operation from BAMBI, 58-62; laying from DUMBO, 63-65, 67; & operation, 64-68; number of BAMBI lines, 61; number of DUMBO lines, 67; assessments, 68, 75; comparison with USA pipe-line, 53; statistics, 79; recovery operation & re-use of parts, 79, 81, 82; relics, 82-84.

HAIS cable coupling & bursting discs - 27, 62, 68, 93-96.

HAIS-HAMEL / HAIS-HAMEL-HAIS combined systems - 66, 67.

Hall, J. & E. Ltd. - 33, 87.

Hamble oil terminal, Hampshire - 44, 69, 83.

HAMEL (Hammick Ellis) steel pipe - concept, 32; code-name, 32; early development, 33, 51; trials, 33-36, 39, 52, 53; manufacture, 35, 39, 87; Tilbury factories, 32, 36; laying from BAMBI, 45, 60,; & operation, 60-62; laying from DUMBO, 65-67; & operation, 67, 68; cross-Solent pipe-line, 44; life expectancy, 33, 68, 75; number of BAMBI lines, 61; number of DUMBO lines, 67; shore ends & connections, 76; comparison with USA pipe-line, 53; assessments, 68, 74, 75; recovery operation & re-use of parts, 81, 82; relics, 82, 84.

Hammick, H. A. - initial concept of flexible steel pipe-line, 32; & development, 33; & Conundrums, 53; Banks on, 74.

Hartley, Arthur Clifford - initial concept of cable pipe-line, 15-18; involvement with HAIS trials, 27, 29; development of cable coupling, 27; & of 3-inch cable, 30, 88, 89; involvement with HAMEL trials, 34; comment on security, 50; as PWD Technical Director, 54; & HAIS-HAMEL, 66; & HAIS bursting discs, 95; Banks on, 74; & statistics, 67, 76; involvement with recovery operation, 81.

Havinden, Captain Ashley - 50.

Heale, Cddr. Treby, RNR - 26, 28, 53.

Hearn, Arthur - 16.

118

Hemixem, Belgium - 104.

Henley's Telegraph Works Co. - cable tests & trials, 22-24, 86; manufacture of cable, 22-23, 31, 39, 86; & of lead piping, 23, 31.

Herentals, Belgium - 104.

History of the Second World War: Civil Histories - 19.

Hitler, Adolf - 39.

Holdfast, HMS (SS *London*) - 26-29, 37, 51, 97.

Holland - 67, 68, 75 (see also specific locations).

Hopper barges - 33, 97.

House-to-house fighting - 45.

Hutchings, Capt. J. F., RN - 37, 51, 63, 80.

Hythe, Kent - 49.

Ilfracombe, Devon - 29.

Illustrious, HMS - 11.

Imperial War Museum - 77, 82, 103.

Iran - 17.

Iraq Petroleum Co. - 32, 87.

Iris, PO telegraph ship - 23. 24.

Isigny, France - 103.

Isle of Wight Electric Light & Power Co. - 87.

Jerricans - 17, 56, 72.

Johnson & Phillips Ltd. - 25, 86.

Joint Administrative Planning Staff - 65.

Judge horizontal lead press - 26, 29.

Juvigny, France - 103.

Kemp, Norman - 16, 29.

Kent - 9, 49, 52 (see also specific locations).

Keyes, Lord - 11.

Kinnear Moodie & Co. Ltd. - 87.

La Londe, France - 72.

Langstaff, Reg - 48.

Largs, Scotland - RATTLE conference, 40, 41; Holywood Hotel, 40.

Latimer, HMS (SS *Empire Ridley*) - 38, 51, 53, 57-59, 64, 79-81, 97.

LCT (tank landing craft) - 28.

Lees, Dr. George - 16.

Le Havre, France - 62, 65.

Lend-Lease Act, 1941 - 55.

Lepe, Hampshire - 34, 40.

Lickens, Maurice - 77, 103, 104, 106.

Lloyd, Geoffrey, MP - takes initial pipe-line initiative, 13-16;
    involvement with trials, 21, 29; re-organises operation, 37; Banks
    on, 74; & statistics, 76.

Lommel, Belgium - 104.

Loobergne, Belgium - 104.

Loubourg, France - 72

Luftwaffe, The - 13, 29, 45.

Lythgoe, Norman - 75.

Maastricht, Holland - 69, 104.

MacPherson, Lieut., RE - 48.

Mainz, Germany - 69.

Manchester Ship Canal Company - 21.

Marauder, HMS - 52.

Marine Contractors Ltd. - 79.

Mather & Platt Ltd. - 87.

Medway, River - 21, 49.

Mersey, River - 15, 44, 69.

Montebourg, France - 70, 103.

Moody Down, Hampshire - 13.

Morgan, Lieut.-General Sir Frederick - 40.

Mountbatten, Admiral Lord Louis - appointed Combined Operations
    Chief, 11, 12; plans for invasions, 12-16, 39-41; & PLUTO, 13-16,
    74.

Mowlem, John & Co. Ltd. - 87.

Mulberry harbours - 9, 39, 52.

Napolean III - 46.
National Physical Laboratory - 22, 34, 52.
National Oil Refineries Ltd. - 27, 86, 87.
Naval Construction, Director of - 27, 36.
New York & seaboard - 55.
Normandy & beaches - 41, 42, 46, 50, 56, 57, 70, 72 (see also specific
    locations).
Nouvelle au Plain, France - 70.

Oil Control Board (Overseas Development Committee) - 16, 18.
Oil policy & administration - 64.
Oil tankers (ocean-going) - 57, 62, 65, 68, 76.
Oil Well Engineering Co. - 87.
Olding, Jack & Co. Ltd. - 87.
OMAHA (invasion) beach - 57.
Orthostyle Ltd. - 36, 87.
Ostend, Belgium - 65, 69, 72, 104.
Ouistreham, France - 103.
Overlord, Operation - 41.

Paris - 62, 69.
Parker, Reg - 47, 70, 77.
Parkhurst Forest, Isle of Wight - 44.
Pas de Calais - 40, 41.
Payton-Smith, D. J. - 64, 66, 67, 74-76.
Pearn, Frank & Co. Ltd. - 87.
Pearn Triple Ram pumps - 71, 72.
Persephone, HMS - 34, 44, 45, 97.
Persephone in mythology - 34.
Petrol consumption - 56.
Petroleum Board - 28, 30, 99.
Petroleum Times - 70.

Whippance Farm pumping station, 44; pipe-line remains, 83, 84.

Tilbury, Essex - 32, 35, 36, 52.

Tip-and-run air raids - 45.

TOMBOLA pipe-lines - 57, 71.

Tombs, H. W. - 27.

Towing tugs - 97.

Trawlers - 97.

TWEEDLEDUM trials, Bournemouth - 52, 53.

U-boats - 13.

USA - cable manufacture, 26, 30, 53, 54; parts manufacture, 55; under sea pipe-line experiments, 53; shipping, 29, 30; forces of liberation, 56-58, 69, 72, 99, 100; First Army Group, 100; fuel supply from, 56, 62 (see also specific locations).

US Engineers - 62, 104.

US Navy - 73.

UTAH (invasion) beach - 70.

Victaulic Co. Ltd. - 87, 105.

Walt Disney studio/characters - 11, 18, 46, 49.

Walton-on-Thames, Surrey - 49, 69.

War Office, The - 16, 21, 37, 67, 81, 99, 100.

War Transport, Ministry of - 26, 51, 79.

Washington DC - 55.

Watermouth Bay, Devon - 29, 30, 39.

Wesel, Germany - 69, 104.

Westward Ho! Devon - 13, 28.

Wight, Isle of - 9, 34, 43-51, 56, 57, 63, 70, 81-84, 106 (see also specific locations).

Woodward, Martin - 82.

Woolwich Works, London - 17, 18, 20-27.

Wormhout, France - 72.

Wright, Dr. H. R. - 16, 18.

Yaverland, Isle of Wight - 46.

NOTE: Personalities are indexed with rank, position, honours etc. as at the time of Operation PLUTO. Later changes, awards etc. - for example, the CBE awarded to Hartley, and the OBEs to Hammick and Ellis for their work on PLUTO - are not shown.